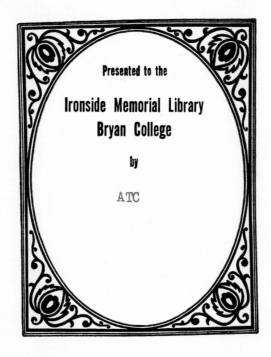

# WIDE MEADOWS

# Wide Meadows

by

Jean Bell Mosley

FOR
Edward and Stephen

# Acknowledgments

Chapter 3 is based on an article entitled "We Learned By the Silver Spoon," copyrighted by *Farm Journal*, September, 1956.

Chapter 4 is based on a story entitled "Dad's Thanksgiving Surprise," copyrighted by *Farm Journal*, November, 1958.

Chapter 5 is based on a story entitled "Snipe Hunt," copyrighted by *Forward*, January 9, 1955.

Chapter 6 is based on a story entitled "Portrait for Molly," copyrighted by *Woman's Day*, November, 1953.

Chapter 7 is based on a story entitled "The Christmas Everyone Cried," copyrighted by *Farm Journal*, December, 1957.

Chapter 8 is based on an article entitled "Christmas in a Country Kitchen," copyrighted by *The Family Herald*, December 22, 1955.

Chapter 9 is based on a story entitled "Winter Visitor," copyrighted by *The Progressive Farmer*, December, 1959.

Chapter 10 is based on an article entitled "Grandpa's A.T. & T." copyrighted by *The Family Herald*, March 12, 1959, and an article, "The Magic Cabinet," copyrighted by *Forward*, May 1, 1955.

Chapter 11 is based on a story entitled "Woman Hater," copyrighted by *The Saturday Evening Post*, January 23, 1954.

Chapter 12 is based on a story entitled "Who Shall We Be Today?" copyrighted by *Evangel*, March 27, 1955.

Chapter 13 is based on a story entitled "The Treasured Wealth," copyrighted by *Farm Journal*, July, 1954.

Chapter 14 is based on a story entitled "Spring Auction," copyrighted by *Forward*, March 28, 1954.

Chapter 16 is based on a story entitled "The Blue-Checked

Linoleum," copyrighted by *The Family Herald,* December, 1953.

Chapter 17 is based on a story entitled "Barbed Wire Geese," copyrighted by *Extension,* August, 1958, and an article entitled "I Learned About Eternity," copyrighted by *Farm Journal,* October, 1958.

Chapter 18 is based on a story entitled "Uncle Joe and the Pulley," copyrighted by *Forward,* November 1, 1953.

Chapter 19 is based on a story entitled "The Republican Fox," copyrighted by *Forward,* November 1, 1953.

Chapter 20 is based on an article entitled "How God Signs His Name," copyrighted by *Faith Today,* September-October, 1954.

# Contents

# WIDE MEADOWS

## Winter Preparations

IN OCTOBER the purple grapes hung high and the hazelnut bushes turned yellow, announcing their gifts were ready. It would be uncomplimentary to Nature not to partake of her lavish provender, so, armed with sacks, buckets and baskets we made our way to the edge of the river pastures for the grapes, up the old woods road for the hazelnuts, hickory nuts and walnuts, and down Plum Thicket Lane to the possum-haunted persimmon patch.

We took only our share, leaving plenty for old Ringtail, the coon, Whitey Possum, the minks, squirrels, jays and other animals and birds that would stay in the valley with us over the winter.

Redtail, the fox squirrel, would watch our maneuvers with bright-eyed suspicion, running up and down the top rail of the fence, cocking his head this way and that, jerking his tail nervously, and chirring noisily at us for entering his domain.

"Now, Redtail," Grandpa would say, placatingly, "you take some of our corn. We take some of your nuts. Therefore, we all have a variety." Whereupon Redtail would scamper to the topmost branch of the old scaly-bark and send down a shower of hulls and cracked shells, silently testifying to the fact that he did not consider it a fair exchange at all. Didn't he have to go all the way down the mountain after the corn and, in the wintertime, even brave the hazards of the barnyard to get to the crib!

The biggest scaly-barks grew on top of Simms Mountain and for this trip we hitched old Maude and Nell to the big wagon, took a well-filled picnic basket, and stayed all day.

High on a hilltop in autumn, looking down on the results of the summer's work—thick shocks of corn with their consorts of yellow pumpkins; the big straw-stack, indicative of the bountiful wheat harvest; fat cattle and peaceful, grazing sheep—we felt compensated for the long, hot summer days recently spent in the fields.

From this height the whole valley was visible—the humble homesteads scattered up and down the river; the railroad track coming out of nowhere around Stono Mountain, making a big two-mile S and disappearing into the nowhere around Gillman's Hill; and the fields, looking like patchwork quilts faggoted together with the stake-and-rider fences. Across the river and up on the first gentle rolling ridge was our home place. There was the barn, the chicken house, the machine shed, and the old, well-loved, gray-weathered, rambling house that sheltered the three generations of us —Grandpa and Grandma, Mama and Dad, and us three girls, Lillian, Lou, and me.

By noon we would have several bushels of hulled nuts and the sun, penetrating the fragrant blue-smoke haze, would have warmed our backs, glistened the sleek rumps of the horses, and made inviting the big flat rock where we spread our dinner.

See! Already Grandma has a pot of coffee on the improvised fireplace. A big brown crock of baked beans centers the red-checked tablecloth, and this is flanked with fried chicken, potato salad, little yellow pear tomatoes, picked before the first frost, and two loaves of freshly baked, yeasty-smelling bread.

Grandpa lifts off the wagon seat for Mama and Grandma to sit in while they eat. He and Dad lean up against the wagon wheels, and we girls sit on piles of leaves or on the filled baskets of nuts.

In the valley below we see Neighbor Stacey leave the cornfield with his wagonload of corn. Next Saturday we will all work in our own cornfield to make up for this week's outing. On down the river we hear Ritter's dinner bell calling the menfolk from work. The whirr of a sawing machine stops and a wagon creaks homeward across the river bridge.

A sudden wind stirs up the ashes of Grandma's fire and brings down a shower of golden leaves. We laugh as we fish them out of our buttermilk and coffee. Autumn is an old friend we can almost take by the hand as she waltzes leisurely through the hills, flitting her red, yellow, and golden skirts and sprinkling harvest perfume in every nook and cranny.

In the afternoon we fill the remaining baskets and have time left over. We have garnered enough for various uncles and aunts, and especially some for Aunt Hannah and Uncle Joe who will come down from St. Louis before long, bearing gifts from the city—

red wool knitting yarn, some plaid flannelette, and maybe a length or two of alpaca for some new dresses.

Grandma ties on a big white apron, brings out her shoebox of quilt scraps she has brought along and works on her Passage-of-Time quilt. She is trying to get it done for a Christmas present. Lou and I roam the mountaintop. There are dry oak balls to squash, a late, green-tailed lizard to watch sunning himself on a ledge, and a great hollow log to explore with a long stick.

"No one home, eh?" Lou says, bending down to look more closely into the log. "Be a good place to run some snipe through," she adds. We have a short game of hull-gull with red berries from the buckbrush and kick up a flurry of leaves, finding three empty, weathered, shotgun shells.

"Play like there has been a murder," Lou says, ominously, "and these are our only clues." She inspects the shells thoroughly, wraps them in her handkerchief, and pockets them professionally, looking around for footprints or other tell-tale signs. A murder mystery has been running serially in our monthly magazine.

The sun slides quickly down the smoky western sky and becomes a big red wagon wheel. Far below in the valley we see the cows head for the barnyard and we load up and start down the mountain.

Blue spirals of smoke rising from neighbors' chimneys bespeak of supper fires and good things to eat, and all is well. There is a chill in the wind now and we are glad to be going home.

This will be our last big outing until spring, for

the days have grown too short for the work that must be done. Thinning maples point accusingly toward the sky. The sassafras is sporting its jewels and the garnet woodbine looks like red wool socks the old trees have pulled halfway up their trunks to protect them from winter's chilly blast. We, too, must think of winter.

The coming of cold weather concerns us much. Enough to eat, comfort and warmth for ourselves and our animals, and a helping hand to less fortunate neighbors is the goal. All summer Mama and Grandma have been filling the cellar shelves. The barn loft bulges with hay. The wheat bin is brimming and now, on crisp October days, we fill the slatted corncrib.

Dad takes a calculating look at the woodpile and decides another load of wood won't hurt anything, so, on a sunny day, up the old woods road we go to bring in extra supplies of pine and hickory slabs. These are unloaded in the woodyard back of the smokehouse and later split into suitable chunks for the various stoves.

With much cramming, maneuvering, and wedging, the machinery is rolled into the lean-to shed. Wheels interlock. Iron teeth bite at steel blades. Wooden tongues overlap. The big binder, its reel touching the rafters, faces east, the wheat drill faces west. The cultivators, rake, and corn planter are heading off in all directions. The whole intermingled mass looks like one Gargantuan machine designed for Paul Bunyan's blue ox, Babe, and calculated to dredge the River Styx, or seed, some night after supper, the whole Plains of Abraham.

Lou and I sit in the cold, perforated, iron seats and whoop at our winged team; we plow, plant, and harvest in one soul-satisfying operation, all the Elysian fields of our youth.

## Gathering the Corn

ALL THE other harvesting efforts pale in stature in comparison with the gathering of the corn. Now we are getting down to business. This is the stuff which will fatten our hogs and feed our chickens and mules, and make nice dents in our debts.

Much of the corn has not been shocked, so down the brown rows we go, scattering bits of stalks and loose shucks right and left, and heaving the fat ears high so that they beat a lively tattoo on the bangboard of the wagon and bounce into the deep bed. We love the good, solid feel of the corn.

"Looka here!" Dad yells, and holds up a fine big ear almost as long as his forearm. We make suitable sounds of acclamation and try to find a bigger one. These finer ears are put away for seed.

Huge flocks of migrating blackbirds alight in the field ahead of us, protesting our coming in squeaky voices. Old crows, from high perches, look down at our operation with wary eyes. "Caw, caw, caw," they cry, in only partial defeat, already casting appraising looks on the adjoining winter wheat field beginning to show green.

Old Shep, matted with cockleburs and laced with

beggar's-lice, strolls up and down the rows, smelling at suspicious hummocks and digging at likely-looking holes. A cottontail springs out from under his very nose and off they go, lickety-split, toward the sassafras thicket in the fence row.

This is the culminating operation of many hours of sweat and toil. It seems long ago since that spring day when Dad crumbled a handful of dirt in his hand and then declared, at the supper table so all could hear, that the ground was ready for plowing. With such an announcement, the corn bread, beans, and potatoes were solemnly passed around again and everyone took a generous second helping, for from then on we'd need all the energy we could muster.

While the mellow bottom fields were being plowed and harrowed, we womenfolk shelled the big ears of corn into a tub and had the seed ready on time. We planted and prayed for rain. The green shoots came peeping through the ground and up went the blue-shirted, behatted, straw-stuffed scarecrow.

Then came the wild morning-glories, cockleburs, and trumpet vines. Hoes were sharpened and muscles became sore. Those days we passed the corn bread, beans, and potatoes three times around.

Eventually the corn is "laid by," and we stand off and look at it appraisingly. "Just one more good rain before the tasseling," Grandpa implores. Up, up, up it goes, way above our heads, and the scarecrow, barely visible now, flaps its frazzled arms in applause.

With no hired hands it takes us about two weeks to gather the corn. If neighbor Ashton is not busy, he and Cabe, his son, will lend us a hand and we will pay him back some way. When the last ear is gathered, we take our places atop the big load for the ride to the crib. Grandpa tosses up the scarecrow and we plunge him deep into the corn so he will stand erect.

There is a new note in Dad's "Giddap there, Maude." The horses seem to know the harvest is in as we make our laughing, bumping, jiggling, flapping way home.

"Let's have a husking party," Lou and I beg. It is to our advantage to do so, for the husking is our task.

We have never had such a party before, but we know the procedure — flickering lantern light, cider and doughnuts, games and songs, and the occasional red ear! My heart flutters in anticipated mortification should my partner find a red ear of corn and I should thus be kissed publicly. But it is not likely, for we seldom have a red ear any more.

"All right," Mama and Grandma agree, so Lou and I take the message to school and the date is set for a Friday night.

That day Mama gets out the big three-legged iron pot, lifts a lid on the stove, and fits the pot snugly into the opening. The best leaf lard, rendered separately, goes into the pot, and doughnut after doughnut is fried to a crisp golden brown until there is a whole mountain of them on the table when we come home from school. Every mug we can muster is washed and dried and carried to the corncrib. Grandpa has gone across the river to bargain for some cider from old Abe Adams, and now the jugs are standing in a row on a shelf in the crib. All is ready.

The neighbors arrive, some on horseback, some in

buggies, but many of them afoot. Most of the young girls and womenfolk have worn their husking gloves, but the menfolk prefer to work without such impedimenta.

First we draw numbers for partners and are paired off in odd couples. I have drawn Mr. Jack, the onetime hobo, for my partner. Lou has drawn bewhiskered old Mr. Crawford.

There are more men than women, so some volunteer to be "women" and pull off the dried corn silk to stick under their caps for long, curly hair. Others, more daring, roll their trouser legs to their knees, revealing knotty limbs sheathed in snug white underwear. There is much hooting and joking and joshing about the fitness of the transformation.

The first pair to reach a hundred ears is to receive a prize, and in this case it is to be two quarts of bread-and-butter pickles. Everybody has bread-and-butter pickles at home, to be sure, but they were not won at the husking bee and therefore cannot be eaten with the accompanying memories of the good fellowship they had there, singing, working, and playing together.

A jovial mood prevails, for cellars and pantries and barns are full, the harvest is over, and God has seen us through another year.

"A-ha," Ray Stacey shouts as he holds aloft a fine red ear. His partner, Miss Mary, the schoolteacher, blushes outrageously, but offers her cheek, which Ray disregards and plants a kiss right on her pretty mouth. There are shouts and claps of approval. Someone starts up a song and all join in. Jeptha Alexander has brought his guitar, so he is excused from husking while he accompanies the rest of us in "Red Wing," "Froggie Went A-Courtin'," and "Sourwood Mountain."

Old Dobbin, in his stall, whinnies uneasily, and cowbells clang in protest at this invasion of the cattle's nocturnal privacy.

"Ha-hoo," Cabe Ashton shouts, and holds high another red ear. We all make signs and sounds of amazement that two red ears have been found. Cabe kisses his partner on the cheek and I die of jealousy, for Cabe is mine.

"Hot ziggety!" exclaims old man Crawford and Lou's eyes grow wide with alarm as he, too, holds aloft a red ear.

"What did you do, Wilson? Plant a whole gallon of red seed so you'd get a kiss?" someone ribs Dad, but he only shakes his head in exaggerated bewilderment.

"Fine crop, Mr. Bell," the farmers say, judiciously, inspecting the plump, uniform ears. Dad replies, "Well, good growing season," and shrugs off all the hours of plowing, planting, cultivating, and harvesting, but that is the way of men of the soil. To them does not belong the glory, but to a Higher Being who provides the sunshine and rain in proper proportion.

Two more red ears are found—three, four—seven, eight! Eight red ears, and all found by the menfolks! Women cluck their tongues at this strange circumstance.

Finally it is all shucked. Around go the refreshments again. Addie Stacey announces hog killing at her home for next Wednesday. Miss Mary says there will be a box supper next Friday at the schoolhouse. Lonnie Britt reminds Mrs. Ritter to send her the recipe for headcheese.

Next day at school Miss Mary asks to borrow a few of the red ears for a decoration she is planning for the box supper, so in the evening I hunt for them, high, low, and middleways, but only one red ear can I find.

"Daddy, I can't find but one red ear," I say, as he sticks his head in the crib door at chore time.

"Well, for goodness sakes," he exclaims, and then brings his eyelid down in a prodigious wink.

"You mean there was only one?" I demand, trying to sound like outraged womanhood.

He nods his head, makes a hushing sound, and brings a peppermint from his pocket, which is a suitable silencing device.

I put the one red ear aside for Miss Mary. No doubt, after the box supper, there will be nothing left but the cob, for all the young boys will have filched a few grains to insure their "crop" for next year.

# The Silver Spoon

NEAR THE close of a cold November day, old Mr. Scroggins stopped in to warm himself by our kitchen fire. He had been chopping wood up in Gold Mine Hollow and was on his way home to his shack down by the river.

"Jeanie," Mama said to me, "fix Mr. Scroggins a cup of tea."

I hastened to do so, reaching for cup and spoon.

"Jeanie." This time Mama spoke severely. "Use the silver spoon."

The silver spoon for old Mr. Scroggins? Why waste it on him, I wondered. But I got it, the only silver spoon we had, and laid it carefully on the saucer. It was delicate and fragile and softly lustrous.

If the silver spoon looked alien in amongst our bone-handled knives and forks in the cabinet drawer, it looked even more so in Mr. Scroggins' calloused old hands. He stirred his tea slowly, looked at the spoon, and then, as if deciding that it was too fine a thing for him to be handling, laid it on the table where it continued to gleam in the lamplight.

Nobody seemed to know just how we acquired the silver spoon. Mama said she had always had it just as Grandma had, and even Great-grandmother. To us it was a symbol of quality and perfection. Lillian, Lou, and I learned to walk by that spoon. Daddy had held the shiny thing out in front of us and we took our first steps toward it. Later, when we were given medicine, we got to use the silver spoon.

"Things are easier done when the tools are pretty and solid and pure," Mama had told us. We thought then that she meant, literally, the silver spoon and pretty dishes and rugs and curtains. But as time went on we came to learn that she meant other things, too —the intangible tools we used every day in living with each other.

Sometimes someone got to eat with the silver spoon. Once Lou had saved her pennies and bought red yarn for Grandma to knit her a pair of mittens, only to have one of Grandma's needles break just as she was ready to begin. Lou exchanged her red yarn for new needles and for that she got to eat with the silver spoon for a whole week!

It was nice to find it by your plate when you didn't know for sure if others had understood the sacrifice you had made, or to find it there as a token that you had been of some help to someone.

Mr. Scroggins drained his cup, mentioned that he'd found a bee tree that day, and took his leave.

After he had gone, Mama explained carefully how mixed up you can become when you try to decide who rates the silver spoon.

"Look at yourself in the spoon," she said. I held it up and looked into the bowl. Whichever way I turned it, I was upside down.

"That's the way you'll always be," Mama said. "Upside down and going around in circles when you try to judge what degree of graciousness you think others rate. When you learn to be as gracious and as kind as possible to all, showing them all the beauty you can, not only in spoons and teacups, but in your real self, you'll look like this."

She turned the spoon over. There I was, right side up.

"What makes it?" I exclaimed.

Of course Mama knew about concave and convex, but why bother with that when she could say, "Well, when you go through sterling and come out on the other side, you just naturally take on some of its qualities and you're bound to be all right."

That night as Lou and I washed the supper dishes I showed her our upside down reflections in the spoons and told her about going through sterling tests in order to come out right side up again on the back.

"Yeah," she said slowly, intrigued with the idea, and we tried to outdo each other in thinking of things that might be classified as sterling tests.

"Carrying water to Grandpa in the summertime," I suggested.

"Going by Britts' bull on our way to school," she added.

"Falling out of the loft."

"Cholera in the hogs."

"Limber-neck in the chickens."

"Selling salve."

"Owing money."

"Snake bite."

# Lights for Thanksgiving

DAD WAS always full of plans and projects. Once he took a look at the old kerosene lamps and said, in the broad expansive manner he employed when launching his many and varied campaigns for the betterment of his family, "These old lamps have to go." His white hair swept back neatly from his forehead and his stance was like Washington crossing the Delaware as he stood there in the old kitchen surveying the lamps. He smiled tolerantly and reminiscently as if they were already on display in a natural setting at some future museum.

"Why, Wilson, whatever on earth do you mean?" Mama asked, stopping her sewing machine only long enough to turn a corner seam. She was making new dresses for Lou and me for the Thanksgiving program at school.

"I mean—" Dad began, and stopped helplessly, waiting for the sewing machine to quiet down again. "I mean we're going to have gas lights," he said, strutting about the museum, peering into the ancient steaming pots to see what was cooking way back then, and waiting patiently for the rest of us, whom he often called "The Practicals," to span the centuries with him.

"It's a carbide system," he explained, when The Practicals continued to lag behind and evinced no measurable amount of interest. After all, we knew we were many miles from a gas line. "You put the carbide and water tank in an outside shed. The water drops onto the carbide forming a gas which is channeled into the house and is turned on and off at the fixture. Just strike a match"—he shrugged his shoulders at the utter simplicity of it—"and what have you? A clear, bright, blue-white flame. No lamp chimneys to clean. No wicks to trim. No constant filling with costly kerosene. No growing up of the children with poor eyesight. Yessiree," he warmed to his plan, twirling his watch fob vigorously, "I mean to bring some light into our lives."

"Well, don't light a match now," Grandma, the Archpractical, said, "or things'll blow up in here for sure with all you're giving out with."

Dad ignored Grandma's remark and walked over to study the Thanksgiving poster Lou and I were working on.

"It's a cornucopia," I explained to Dad in much the same manner as he was trying to explain his gas lighting system, half-fearful that in the advanced century in which he seemed to be living they had done away with Thanksgiving. "It is symbolic of peace and plenty and purple autumn haze—and burning leaves and frost on the pumpkin."

"All that?" Dad asked, an appreciative look in his pale blue eyes. He took the poster up and looked a bit more closely. "Sure enough," he exclaimed, "and I can further see the squirrels and chipmunks busy storing their food, corn shocks, a harvest moon, and the mallards flying south. And listen," he said, excitedly, holding the poster up to his ear, "hear that cricket?"

It was actually a cricket we'd been hearing all fall somewhere about the kitchen fireplace, but it was good to play this game with Dad. And it was comforting to know that there still must be a Thanksgiving up ahead.

"Let's try these on now," Mama said, holding up the partially finished dresses. "When is all this light supposed to come into our lives, Wilson?" she asked absently, measuring a hem.

Dad studied the ceiling and the view from several kitchen windows before replying. He did a little figuring on the back of an envelope, walked over to the calendar and flipped a few pages, and when the sewing machine quieted down again, said, "Next week." This was in his clipped, climactic, closing-in voice he used when it was necessary to rouse The Practicals out of their lethargy, inertia, opposition, rebellion, or despair, which he said we often suffered epidemically.

Mama spun around, removing pins from her mouth hurriedly. Such haste in Dad's plans she was not used to meeting.

"Next week?" she demanded. "Now, Wilson, a thing like that takes time and money."

"Money, yes. Time—no. The whole system can be installed in a day. We'll set the tank in the smokehouse. We'll all lend a hand at digging the ditch and we'll start with just the one fixture right here in the kitchen. Right about here." He climbed up on the table, turning over the sugar bowl, and marked a little circle on the ceiling with his pencil. "We'll have it ready for Thanksgiving and we'll ask all the neighbors in. They'll be green-eyed with envy."

"I thought the purpose of the thing was for better eyesight, not to turn the neighbors green-eyed with envy," Mama said, rather sharply, and Grandma, from the dark confines of the pantry, offered a remote and muffled approval of Mama's crisp reply.

"Well, someone in the community has to make a step forward." Dad knocked the spoon holder over getting down. "We been going on and on with the same old beliefs and customs and lighting systems generation in, generation out." He had reached the table-pounding stage, only used when The Practicals seemed impenetrable, and I watched Mama's little pile of pins do an Indian war dance.

"All right. All right!" Mama said, hastily cupping her hand over the pins. "But will the neighbors want to come on Thanksgiving? That's a family day when folks like to be around their own table."

"They'll come," Dad said, nodding his head affirmatively, "when I hint there's going to be a demonstration of something for the betterment of the community."

"Well, let's see now," Mama started planning. "We'll have roast turkey with chestnut dressing, cauliflower au gratin, fluted patty shells with creamed peas—"

"—and gravy, bread and potatoes," Grandma joined in, flatly practical.

Dad disappeared and returned shortly with his

brace and bit and the benign smile of one way out
in front. He climbed up on the kitchen table again
and began boring a hole right in the center of the
ceiling while The Practicals looked on with puckered
brows. Lou and I watched the curly wood borings
come drifting down like soft, blond snowflakes.

"Well, it sure does need airin' out in here," Grandma said, breaking the uncomfortable silence that followed the hole-boring. "We could have opened the
door, though," she added ruefully, looking up at the
fresh new hole leading into the attic.

"H-umph," Dad remarked.

Some of the borings fell into the spilled sugar and
Mama picked them out daintily.

"You don't suppose mice can come down through
there, do you, Myrtle?" Grandma asked Mom, like she
never expected to have the hole stopped up with anything ever again. Mama said perhaps not, but the
attic mud daubers were sure to come.

"H-umph," Dad reiterated. It wasn't that he had
a limited vocabulary. It was just that if he'd said
anything more, Grandma and Mama would start discussing, interestedly, what they might do with the
bathtub Dad had fashioned once and couldn't get in
through the doorway when he had it finished; or the
long, gasoline-driven, conveyor belt that was supposed
to deliver heavy things from the barn to the house.
It would have worked, except that the belt swayed
in the middle under the weight of a bucket of milk
or a basket of eggs, the only heavy things we had to
transport from the barn to the house.

The carbide lighting system was a used one for sale

at Wallingford's Mercantile. It could be had for one fat steer and a wagonload of corn which Dad had calculated were expendable.

Lou and I went to town with Dad in the big wagon and actually saw the exchange take place. He covered the tank and pipes and fixtures with old quilts. "Don't want no one asking questions," he explained, winking, comrade-like, at us. He meant the neighbors we would probably see on our way home. Lou and I swelled with pride in our forward-looking father's actions as he loudly and loftily informed various and sundry strangers in and about the store of what he was doing, not only for the immediate family, but that his action would serve as a lever to lift the whole community out of a generation's old rut. This, I felt, with a secret thrill in my heart, would cancel the abortive bathtub and conveyor belt and make Mama stop the sewing machine when Dad had something to say—and keep Grandma from dodging the mud-daubers in such a theatrical manner. They had begun to come down through the hole, seeking the warmth of the kitchen.

Paul Britt was making a few repairs on his rickety old barn when we passed by his farm. The whole Britt place was rickety and run-down and scrawny-looking. A few years ago a windstorm that had skipped every other place in the community had crippled the barn and twisted the house on the foundation. Paul had never recovered because, as he said, he "couldn't find a startin' point." It was a joke to make light of the disaster and everyone went along with it, offering suggestions to Paul all the time as to where he should begin his restoration.

"I'd start with a match and some coal oil," Jim Stacey suggested, and Tom McDowell said the easiest way to get on top again, in his opinion, would be just to plow the whole place under.

"Howdy, Paul," Dad greeted, pulling the horses to a stop. "Found a startin' place?"

"Naw, sir, I ain't, Wilson. Thought sure I had. I says to myself only this morning, 'Now, it's on the west side of the barn you need to start—she's a-leanin' westward.' So I started bracin' it back up and now I got it a-leanin' eastward. They just ain't no proper startin' place."

"How about starting with Thanksgiving?"

"Thanksgiving?" Mr. Britt laughed as if it were a joke. "For this?" He let his arm sweep over the sorry sight that was his homestead.

"Well, you got the land yet," Dad observed.

"No, I reckon I ain't right properly got the land no more. Third year the taxes have gone unpaid and you know that can't go on forever."

"No, it can't, Paul," Dad agreed, "but, anyway, I was going to say, how about you and Lonnie having Thanksgiving dinner with us this year? I'm asking the neighbors in. Got a little surprise to spring."

"Oh, I reckon not, Wilson. We'd be pretty poor company around a Thanksgiving table knowing this was probably our last year here. Sure hate to be leaving, but don't see no way out of it."

Dad looked gloomier than Mr. Britt. "Well, sure like to have you if you change your mind, Paul."

Mrs. Stacey was digging parsnips when we arrived there. Dad got down and went over to the fence, and Lou and I followed.

"Bessie, how about you all coming over and having Thanksgiving dinner with us next week?"

"Thanksgiving?" Mrs. Stacey's chin started trembling. "Oh, Wilson, we just couldn't. This'll be the first year we've not all been together and we'll not be fit company on Thanksgiving. If only Jack could be home, but we can't send him the coming money." The tears started running down Mrs. Stacey's cheeks. Lou and I started crying, too. We'd been flower girls at her other son's funeral during the past year and the sadness all seemed to come back.

"Got a little surprise I was a-fixin' to show the neighbors," Dad said, wistfully. "Something the whole community might like to adopt."

Mrs. Stacey just shook her head miserably. We climbed back into the wagon and went on. Dad's shoulders began to sag and wrinkles formed across his forehead. This was unexpected interference with his plans.

The McDowells were just sitting down to noonday dinner when we reached their house. There were Tom and Polly and Herbert and Aileen and Maggie all around the table. We looked for the rest of them, but didn't see them anywhere.

"Well, Wilson, howdy." Tom got up and shook Dad's hand heartily. "Get, some of you kids, and let these folks sit down and eat with us."

Dad protested, but neither Tom nor Polly would hear to our not stopping to eat. There was a great bowl of potatoes cooked in their jackets centering the table. Each person took a potato as it was passed, and that was dinner.

Dad made a great ceremony of peeling, salting, peppering and eating his potato, so Lou and I did too.

"Want you all to come over to our house for Thanksgiving dinner." Dad issued his invitation.

Tom and Polly exchanged worried glances.

"Don't reckon we can, Wilson. Got some sick kids on my hands." He motioned toward the bedroom.

"What's the trouble?" Dad asked.

"Well, it ain't something you can put your finger on like the grippe or measles or snake bite. Doc says it's a longtime thing and that the kids need more fruit and things."

"Sure am sorry," Dad said. "Had a little surprise I was a-fixin' to show the folks. Well, come if you can."

We almost got home with the lighting system. We had crossed the river and started up the last long hill. Our place looked like a Thanksgiving poster itself, I thought. How nice it would be to have the new lights and with the new lights a new, respectful family relationship. It would be the best Thanksgiving ever.

Suddenly Dad turned the wagon around and sent the horses on a trot back to town.

"What did you forget?" Lou asked, but he didn't answer. Back to Wallingford's we went and to our great amazement heard Dad tell Mr. Wallingford he didn't want the lighting system after all and would Mr. Wallingford please give him back his money, only keep out enough to send a barrel of oranges and apples out to a family by the name of McDowell on the Elvins-to-Loughboro road. Then Dad went to the depot and the courthouse to transact some Thanksgiving business, he said. Lou and I sat huddled in the wagon, miserable about the great retreat. Now Grandma and Mama would have the hole in the ceiling to talk about, along with the bathtub and belt, and there it would be, right over our heads three times a day.

It was after dark when we got back home and snowing softly. The lamps, stationary, hanging, and bracketed, sent light streaming from the kitchen windows, turning the snow to gold dust and making a welcome path for us. How nice things could have been if we were just coming home from an ordinary Saturday trip to town!

Well, there were certain sterling tests one had to go through, Lou and I reminded each other.

Mom and Grandma were silent about the lighting system, which made it look more than ever like they didn't expect anything Dad planned to come about. I wanted to say, "Well, he did get it and almost got home with it, but—but—" My upholding of Dad's actions seemed to sway in the middle like the conveyor belt.

Everyone carefully avoided looking at the hole in the ceiling for the next several days. Once Grandma, after having swept, stuck the broom handle up through it and said maybe we could use it for a broom holder if we moved the table. It looked ridiculous hanging down over the table. I jerked it down and put it where it belonged and Grandma told Mom she believed I needed a round of sulphur and molasses.

"Guess the neighbors won't be coming for Thanksgiving," Dad told Mama and Grandma when preparations for the meal were getting underway. He didn't say why and they didn't ask, not even about the fat steer and the wagonload of corn that had disappeared.

Lou and I were proud of our new dresses as we stood up to say our Thanksgiving pieces. Everything Mama did, she did well. It was artistic, neat, finished, and workable.

The pies she made Thanksgiving morning were brown and flaky. The turkey was roasted to golden perfection. The potatoes were light and puffy. It wasn't her fault that there wasn't enough to go around for Dad had said the neighbors weren't coming. But they did. All of them.

"I know it weren't right of us to come in on you at the last minute, Myrtle," Mrs. Stacey said, handing Mom two loaves of freshly baked bread, "but after Jack came home, surprisin' us like he did, we couldn't keep from comin'. And don't act like you don't know where his ticket came from." She pushed Mama gently on the shoulder and winked secretly.

Lonnie Britt set down a jar of preserves and hugged Mama, saying that a more neighborly thing could never have been done than what we had done about the taxes. And as soon as they got on their feet again they'd pay them back.

Mama sat down weakly. She glanced at Dad and I saw him nod his head the least little bit of a nod. And Mama suddenly smiled at him. A symbolic smile, I guess you could say, like Dad's cricket and the cornucopia. It said, *I love you, and I think what you've done is wonderful.*

Grandma opened some more cans of beans and peaches and preserves and cut all the pieces of pie in two again. We brought in the library table and the bedside tables and all the boxes and benches we could find, and had a wonderful meal.

"Now, Wilson," Paul Britt said, when everyone was finished, "tell us what your surprise is."

Dad looked stunned. I guess he'd forgotten he'd promised a surprise.

"You mean you ain't seen it yet?" Grandma said, pointing ruthlessly to the hole in the ceiling.

I watched nineteen pairs of eyes turn toward the hole in the ceiling, then toward each other and finally toward Dad. I felt so sorry for him I couldn't stand it. I pretended to drop something on the floor and got down to hunt for it so I wouldn't have to watch these people laughing at him, destroying his dignity.

"It's a symbolic hole," I heard someone say, and I got up off the floor hurriedly to see who else understood this kind of stuff. It was Grandma.

"It stands for light that Wilson, here, has brought into our lives. All of us have holes in our lives, don't we?" She looked around at the folks slowly. "Holes where something isn't that we had planned to be," Grandma continued in a very practical voice. "And we have to fill them up with something else until the right thing comes along."

A queer feeling took hold of me, hearing Grandma, the Archpractical, talking like this. A good, light, floating feeling. I looked at the hole in the ceiling again and thought of how it was filled up with Jack Stacey's railroad ticket home and Paul Britt's three years of taxes, and a barrel of fruit rather than with the carbide light fixture for which Dad had made it.

"And," I heard Archpractical going on, warming to her explanation, "sometimes the things we fill holes with turn out to be better than the thing we had intended for them."

Dad was glowing like a pumpkin in the autumn sun. Mrs. Stacey and Mrs. Britt had caught on and were using their napkins as handkerchiefs. Sad-happy they were. I'd felt like that before, too. Mr. Britt, looking thoughtful, had thrown back his shoulders like he had found a startin' point at last.

"You mean you bored that hole there a-purpose for this lesson?" Mr. McDowell demanded, skeptically, ready to laugh at the joke that must be here somewhere.

"We're using it for that until something better comes along," I said.

Everything got so quiet.

Dad scraped back his chair and went over to open the door. "Needs airin' out in here a little, don't you think?" he asked everyone, but Archpractical especially.

November sun flooded in, laying a golden floor mat before the door, but it did not match the illumination that came to everyone, especially to us, through the hole to the attic.

# Pork Roast and Snipe

THE ONE remaining major undertaking before Christmas is butchering. In the spring the hogs were turned loose in the hills, their ears marked with varying notches for later identification, and cautioned to "Root, hog, or die." In the late summer or early fall, they were rounded up, penned, and fattened with corn and other supplements.

When the weather is just right, warm enough so that the meat will take salt, yet cold enough to prevent spoilage, we proceed with the butchering. But not before suitable rituals and small flourishes that make all tasks lighter and give a fine sense of having done a job well.

This calls for a cleanup of the smokehouse, resurrection of the hairscrapers, making of the gambrel sticks, and the sharpening of all knives, both large and small.

It is deemed too dangerous to render the lard in the house, so Grandma scrubs the big iron kettle, settles it on the stand under the back-yard cherry tree, and sees that a supply of slow-burning wood is near at hand. The sausage grinder is washed and scalded and screwed securely to the side of a board which is fastened onto wooden horses of sufficient height so that a washtub can be fitted in under the grinder to receive the meat. Thus, a person can work astraddle the board, or stand up and grind as he chooses.

Our smokehouse was of large, hand-hewn logs, neatly notched and fitted at the corners and chinked with a mud and hair plaster. It was originally roofed with hand-riven shingles, but storms and weather having taken their toll, we later put a tar-paper covering over the shingles. Old Man Adams, the valley historian, said the smokehouse was much older than our house and, indeed, it was large enough for the common one-room log cabin of earlier days, but there was no fireplace so we discounted the theory that it was once used as a home.

There were no windows, but in places the chinking had fallen out and left little peepholes of light. A great, split sycamore log, turned rounded side up, served as the step before the heavy plank door. At the far end, away from the door, a wide shelf was built crosswise from wall to wall. Here we laid the big hams and shoulders, middlings and jowls, while they took salt. Later on they were suspended from crossbeams while the smoking process went on.

Most major undertakings of this sort were begun on Monday, so on Sunday afternoon we lay more groundwork for the eventful day. On the hillside sloping down to the creek, not far from the hogpen, was a large maple with a suitable crotch of proper height to support one end of the heavy log that is erected, from which to hang the hogs. The other end is held up by a thick railroad tie, properly notched. A big

wooden barrel, lying on its side, is set at an angle
to hold water, yet easily receive the hairy carcasses of
the hogs. This is accomplished by digging an inclin-
ing depression in the ground and securing the barrel
therein.

Lou and I bring up big rocks from the creek, and
old, broken plowshares and other pieces of iron from
the tool shop, and lay them alongside the firewood.
On the morrow the fire will be built the first thing,
even before breakfast or milking. The rocks and old
pieces of iron will be put into the fire and later pulled
out with a hoe and transferred, via a long-handled
shovel, to the water in the barrel. The water must
be scalding hot before the hair will scrape easily from
the hogs.

The neighbor men help with the butchering just
as they do at haying and threshing. Later Grandpa
and Dad will go to their homes to help them. Fresh
sausage, liver, backbones, and ribs are shared with
each other at the successive "hog killin's."

On the day of the big event, Lou and I do our chores
early and hurry off to school so as not to hear the
goings-on at the pigpen. When we come back, late
in the evening, the big, white, split carcasses will be
suspended from the log and we will not be able to
tell Old Flea-hide from Flop-ear.

After supper we will go to the cold smokehouse and
work by lantern light, turning the sausage grinder,
while Dad and Grandpa trim the hams and shoulders
and square up the middlings, and Mama and Grandma continue their task of stripping fat for lard.

But we don't mind the cold, for we are in conspiratorial cahoots against future hunger, and there is a comfortable camaraderie as we grind and slice and salt. Grandpa hands Grandma a sow's ear and says, "Here's your silken purse." She throws a pigtail at him.

This year we will butcher a hog for the Kotiskis, a new family in the cabin on Gillman's Hill. Staceys will provide for old Granny Weaver, and other provident neighbors will share with others less fortunate. All this has been decided earlier at a Sunday afternoon meeting of the menfolks at Old Man Adams', a favorite gathering place.

It seemed fitting and proper that we should provide for the Kotiskis in view of previous entanglements with that family, and truth to tell, our generosity was tinged with a little self-defense at being asked to their house for a meal.

The Kotiskis were a part of the great influx of migrant families into the Ozarks. Tie cutters they were. Men who could not, by any combination of their plodding brain cells, fathom the number of cubic feet in a rank of wood or calculate the circumference of a stump other than that it was so many hands around, but who could drive a potent wedge, make their own go-devils, swing an accurate ax, and manage by hook or crook to keep their big families round-cheeked, bright-eyed, and clothed—with the aid of a great many safety pins.

The Kotiskis made an odorous advent into the community. Of our family, Lou and I were the first to be introduced to this alien tribe, not too long removed from their native country.

It was during a study period one morning at school. The door latch rattled ominously. The hinges squeaked stealthily. The door opened cautiously, and inch by inch a shaggy blond half head came into view with one round, bright, unwinking blue eye peering around the jamb. After a cursory inspection it was quickly withdrawn and soon another, smaller, shaggier blond half head inched into view. And yet a third surveyed the room suspiciously, one-eyed.

"Won't you come in?" Miss Mary invited pleasantly.

With that the door was slammed, and we heard hurriedly retreating footsteps on the gravel walk. Evidently they had gone off to hold council as to the desirability of taking on this community custom of going to school.

Some three days later the trio emerged from the bushes surrounding the playground at recess and stood silently watching us play "ante over."

"Don't say anything," the teacher cautioned, and we went on with our game while the blond Kotiskis edged closer and closer. Once the ball rolled to the feet of the biggest boy and, on being urged to "throw it here," he picked it up and flung it toward the group.

Recess was overtime that day—long enough to draw the two strange boys and their sister into our group —and when the bell rang, they followed the rest of us into the schoolhouse.

Anna Kotiski, being in about the fifth grade, she thought, was seated in the empty seat across the aisle from me. Jon, the biggest boy, was placed in the eighth grade, and Flemm in the seventh.

The water bucket was passed, the big hooded stove

generously stoked, and we settled down to work, the Kotiskis suffering agonies of embarrassment as the rest of us stared in frank curiosity. Soon questioning eyes looked into questioning eyes, eyebrows shot upward, surreptitious sniffs were heard from all corners of the room. Windows were raised a little at a time. Finally, Paul Ritter, always outspoken, demanded: "Phew! What is that smell in here?"

No one knew. Teacher asked someone to look on top of the stove for anything burning. Cabe and Sam, two of the bigger boys, went to look under the schoolhouse for a dead rabbit or something. The Kotiskis were as innocent as the rest. How could they know we were not used to garlic being eaten for breakfast, or asafetida worn around the neck in little brass filigree lockets to ward off the flu?

The offending strangers further enhanced their unpopularity by bringing no lunches to school, other than a large turnip or two, which Anna peeled with a great deal of deliberation and doled out in slices to her brothers. Sometimes a pocketful of ripe persimmons in varying degrees of squashiness served as dessert. These were gobbled hurriedly. Then Anna and the smaller boy would turn large unblinking eyes on the sandwiches, cake, cookies, and apples the rest of us brought. They never asked for anything but just sat there watching, following the food with their eyes. You could turn your back but still feel their eyes coming through, and finally, in desperation, you offered them part of your lunch, which was readily accepted, chewed, swallowed, and the unblinking vigil resumed.

Ridiculous stories were circulated about the Kotiskis to the effect that the father's body was hairy all over like an ape's. The mother was—well, no one believed in witches any more, but she had been seen out at midnight roaming the hills with a basket gathering all sorts of things—terrapins, oak balls, toadstools. They said she wore a spider in an empty walnut shell around her neck.

"Oh, pshaw!" Mama scoffed disgustedly and warned us to be nice to the Kotiskis and take no part in the silly talk.

"Just remember," she cautioned, "we are a part of all we know"—she had that underlined somewhere in a book—"so now that you know the Kotiskis, why don't you take from them their good part?"

Lou and I walled our eyes at each other, wondering what was the good part. Jon knew how to hold his galluses up with a nail. Anna could get along without handkerchiefs—she used her striped flannelette petticoat. And Flemm could spit a persimmon seed and hit the wood box from twenty feet away.

Mama, determined to show good neighborliness, went calling on Mrs. Kotiski with two loaves of freshly baked bread, and she said she couldn't see that she was much different from anybody else. They were finding our country a little strange, perhaps, but were adapting themselves to it, probably better than we could adapt ourselves to theirs. "It's up to us to introduce them to the customs of our country," she said.

We conferred with our friends at school about this and decided that nothing could be more American than taking the Kotiski boys on a snipe hunt.

"And I know just the log to use," Lou exclaimed.

A quick smile of pleasure passed over Jon's face when we asked him if he would join us that night for the hunt.

"What's a snipe?" he asked.

"Haven't you ever seen a snipe?" Cabe asked incredulously.

Jon scratched his head with labored thinking but reluctantly admitted that he'd never seen a snipe. "But I'm a good hunter, and Flemm, too," he added hastily, for fear we would withdraw the invitation. "Just tell us what they look like and if one comes close, we'll shoot it all right."

"Oh, you don't shoot these," Paul explained with earnest and elaborate patience, giving a so-and-so measurement of the height and length of this fictitious American animal. Lou and I nodded in solemn agreement.

"First, you find their runs. You know what a run is, don't you?" Cabe asked.

The blond shaggy heads nodded vigorously. Sure, they knew what runs were.

"Well, two people or more—better just two people though—hide on their runs, holding an open sack, and the others get behind on the trail and drive the snipe into the sack."

The Kotiskis shook their heads in tolerant amusement at such funny American hunting.

"They good to eat?" Flemm asked.

"Oh, sure! The best," Cabe assured them. "Little salt and pepper—"

It was cold that night—a clear, still cold. There

was a hard crust of snow and ice on the river. We met at the swinging bridge and did a little shoe-sole skating first.

"They don't come out till 'bout nine o'clock," Cabe explained to Jon and Flemm, and the rest of us giggled silently into our mufflers.

"You bring your sack?" Paul asked.

The Kotiskis displayed an old tow sack for our inspection.

"Ought to be all right," Cabe said, holding it up to the moonlight. "Well, let's get started."

Jon and Flemm were stationed at the end of that hollow log on top of Simms Mountain with their sack.

"For some reason or other they like to run through logs," Cabe told them, generously sharing his knowledge of snipe hunting. "Now, it may take some time for us to drive them this way, but don't give up."

The Kotiskis nodded in understanding and made replies indicative of their stanchness.

"Who gets the snipe?" Jon hollered after us.

"Oh, you can have them," we chorused.

"Well, thanks," came the reply.

Far enough away, we stopped to give freedom to our mirth and to contemplate the expressions of chagrin on the Kotiskis' faces on the morrow. After assuring each other that we had done our part in introducing them to a great American country custom and speculating hilariously on just how long they would stay there, we went our homeward ways to warm beds and a good night's sleep.

It was the consensus that the Kotiskis would slip into school the next day unobtrusively and as silently as possible, red-faced and hangdog. But they made their usual blustery entrance, letting in cold air and a flurry of snow, and, as always, accompanied by their terrible aura of smells. Today it was even worse. Their heads were held high, but their faces were satisfyingly red. After closer inspection you could say the Kotiskis were aglow.

Jon and Flemm flashed wide, friendly, toothy grins and held up two fingers in a triumphant gesture.

Baffled expressions were exchanged over the schoolroom. A few notes were guardedly passed up and down the aisle, wanting to know what was up. I asked to speak to Anna and whispered, "How did they come out?"

"They got two," she replied, looking pridefully at her brothers.

"Two what?" I demanded.

"Snipe, you call them."

I would have pressed her further but today the garlic, asafetida, and whatever else were too powerful.

At recess Cabe and Paul began on them. "Well, how you like snipe hunting?" they asked, mocking laughter in their eyes.

"Fine, fine," Jon said. "They didn't run into the sack, though. We clubbed 'em like we always do."

"Oh, yeah?"

Things weren't coming off as everyone had planned.

"Like to go again, I guess?" Cabe asked.

"Sure. Anytime," Jon replied. There was only friendliness and good will in his voice. He and Flemm could not understand just why we were all so skeptical about their having caught the snipe. I couldn't help admiring the way they had turned the tables on us.

No use in carrying it so far, though, I thought, when Mama told Lou and me when we got home from school that Mrs. Kotiski had called that day and invited us all up for a snipe supper the next evening, since we had been so nice as to help show the boys how to catch them.

"You see?" Mama said. "She can take a joke just like the rest of us."

"Are we going?" Lou demanded.

"Why, of course we're going," Mama said.

"We could all get sick," Lou suggested, brightening.

"But we're not sick," Mama said, her eyes beginning to flash. "And when neighbors are kind enough to ask us for a meal, we must go. We're probably the first she has ever asked."

We thought this a dubious honor.

"Wonder what she'll have to eat?" Lou said, suppressing a shudder.

Mama made us put on our best dresses and patent-leather shoes. Dad curried the team, and we set off in style that evening, with scrubbed faces and freshly braided hair.

"Is the good neighbors!" Mrs. Kotiski shouted back to her household as she ran to meet us. Mr. Kotiski came out and very solemnly shook hands with every one of us, shifting a toothpick from one side of his mouth to the other.

"Come in, please?" Mrs. Kotiski asked, as if she still doubted we had come a-calling. She would walk a few steps ahead, then turn anxiously to see if we were still following.

Lou and I were expecting to be stifled in the small house with so many Kotiskis under one roof, for besides Jon, Flemm, and Anna, there were two more little ones at home. However, it wasn't so bad. There was a pleasant aroma of roasting meat. If snipe smelled like that while cooking, then we would have some! We suspicioned they had rounded up someone's hog that roamed the hills and butchered it.

Mrs. Kotiski had set one long table in the living room. There were only four chairs, but plenty of upturned boxes and long benches. There were forks and knives at some places, and she saw to it that we were seated there. Lacking a tablecloth, she had spread colored comic sections of the paper on the table, and we thought that was clever.

First came a big bowl of turnips, which she set in the middle of the table; then a bowl of turnip slaw to one side of that, and then the *pièce de résistance* —snipe! We each took a piece, anxious to see just what it was.

"Squirrel," I whispered to Lou.

"Too big," she murmured under her breath. "Must be rabbit."

Dad's brows were knit in questioning concentration as he took his first bite. He looked at Mama, who was also thoughtfully chewing.

"Catching many possums?" Dad asked brightly, turning to Mr. Kotiski.

"Is the ones who play like dead?"

Dad nodded.

"No. No luck with possum."

Dad took another bite. "Saw lots of coon tracks down by the river the other day."

"Coon? They good to eat?" Mrs. Kotiski asked, passing us the salt and pepper.

"Some folks do," Dad said.

"Better than snipe?" Mrs. Kotiski asked, gnawing on a piece of rib. "We don't call 'em snipe back home."

Dad only laughed but stole a baffled look at Mama.

Well, whatever it was, it was pretty good, I thought. There wasn't a piece left.

After supper Mama helped Mrs. Kotiski with the dishes. Dad and Mr. Kotiski talked about the price of railroad ties. Jon and Flemm taught Lou and me some strange game they played on something like a checkerboard. Soon it was time to go home, for tomorrow was another school day, and we had to report on the snipe supper to Cabe and Paul and the others.

Mr. Kotiski lit his lantern and showed us out to the surrey.

"Is skins any good here?" he asked Dad.

"What skins?"

"Snipe skins."

"Oh," Dad laughed. "Kids will have their fun, won't they?"

Mr. Kotiski's brow furrowed with his labored attempt to understand.

"Come," he motioned with his lantern and led Dad off behind the woodshed. Lou and I followed. We had an interest here.

"My boys know how to remove the sacks on these-here 'snipe,' as you call them. That makes the skins better, and you couldn't eat them any other way," Mr. Kotiski said, holding the lantern high. And there, nailed up, shining in the bright circle of light, were two of the prettiest skins you ever saw; bushy tails; long, silky hair; shiny, jet-black fur—with white stripes right down the middle of the backs!

# A Gift for Molly

WINTER comes down from the mountains in a white fury and locks the valley tight in its icy grip. The river slows and comes to a frozen stop. Icicles fringe the eaves of the buildings and a tiny one hangs from Grandpa's moustache when he comes in from the barn. The pumps freeze. The wood box is in constant need of refilling and we stamp and sputter and blow and allow, in heavy understatement, as how it is right smart cold outside.

Old Nell and Maude make velvet whinnies in their stalls and the cows, their shaggy winter hair portentous of bleak days ahead, munch tunnels far back into the haystacks.

The cold north wind, rebuffed by battened windows, shakes the old house till it creaks and groans, and blows cold breath down the chimney ways. Then softly in the night comes the eider-downy blanket of snow to mute the sounds and put soft white tam-o-shanters atop the fence posts and old field stumps.

By their comings and goings, furry animals, with softly padded feet, stitch together, in the night, the fields and roads and frozen streams as though the valley were in danger of ripping apart.

The word "Christmas" creeps into our conversation and we begin, early, wrapping glasses of jelly, buckets of maple syrup, and boxes of nuts, for some of the city folks may make just one more trip to the farm before Christmas (the roads are well nigh impassable afterwards), and we will have their presents ready, however early. Lou and I begin to cast calculating eyes at cedar trees, choosing this one, discarding that one. There is a wealth to choose from. But we do not go after the tree until the last present is wrapped and tied. For Mama and Grandma we have embroidered dresser scarves. For sister Lillian we have made blue and pink satin-covered garters, lace-trimmed. For Grandpa and Dad we pool our pennies and purchase a fat pouch of tobacco. For each other we may have crayolas, a powder puff, or a can of violet-scented talcum powder.

Grandma has been working long hours on her Passage-of-Time quilt, and at last it is in the frames ready to be quilted. But, I remember, all was not well with Grandma at this particular Christmas. She was worried. Molly Layton was coming to the Christmas quilting party and Grandma had no gift for her. For all the other ladies she had made little presents—lacey-edged handkerchiefs, quilted pot holders, needlecases, patchwork pillow tops, but for Molly she had made nothing because she hadn't known Molly was coming.

It was more than a year now since Molly had worked for us and the other neighbor ladies, helping with the house cleaning, canning, and cooking. She had left as suddenly as she had come and no one had

heard from her since, not until now, when Mrs. Stacey
had called up on the day of the quilting party to ask
if we remembered Molly Layton and to say that she
was there at her house and wanted to come along to
help with Grandma's Passage-of-Time quilt.

We remembered Molly, all right. One summer day
she had walked in off the road—run-over shoes, skimpy,
faded dress, a large mole on her nose, straight, sun-
faded hair hooked behind her ears—and announced
that she had come to do our sewing. When she spoke,
we saw that one of her front teeth was missing.

"But I do my own sewing," Mama had told her.
"You must have the wrong place."

"No, ma'am," she said, putting her hand over her
mouth to hide the defect. "I'll do your cookin', then."

"We-ll," Mama faltered, puzzled at this strange girl.
"We got plenty of cooks." She motioned to us girls
and Grandma.

"Cleanin'?" Molly asked.

Mama shook her head and said nothing.

"Milkin', then. What about milkin'?" Molly asked.

"Good land! We all milk," Mama replied.

Molly turned then and walked forlornly back to the
gate. Her thin shoulders under the faded dress seemed
to droop even lower, and we saw her wipe her arm
across her eyes as she hooked her fallen hair back
over her ear.

"Wait a minute," Mama called as Molly fumbled
with the latch. "Come back and have a bite of gingerbread and a glass of milk, anyway."

Molly blew her nose noisily and came back. "Excuse me, ma'am," she said apologetically, for the tears, "but I sure do need a job."

"Well, just sit and rest a while and have a bite to eat. You look all tuckered," Mama said.

"I guess I ought to be. I started out day before yesterday morning, and I've stopped at every house I've seen, and nobody wants any work done, and now I'm way out in the country, where the houses are far apart." The tears started again.

"Where's your folks?" Mama inquired.

"Just me left. That's all." Molly gave a long shivering sigh.

"Well, we're canning beans tomorrow. Maybe you could help us," Mama said.

So Molly stayed for the canning, and then the threshers came and she stayed on to help cook, and then it was time to put up the peaches. We couldn't pay her much, but she carefully hoarded her money. She was going to have the mole taken off, a new tooth put in, and get some water-wave combs for her hair. "Of course I could get the combs right away, but they wouldn't help much with this face. Ain't I the ugliest thing you ever saw?" Molly would deride herself, trying to be gay about it and acting as if it didn't matter. But it hurt. You could tell that by the way she'd look at herself in the mirror, fluff her hair out speculatively, and then turn away.

And she appreciated beautiful things. On Sundays, when we used Grandma's rose-sprigged china, she would hold a dish up to the light and say, "Aren't they the most beautiful things you ever saw?" She'd wipe the plates lovingly and stack them with tissue

paper in between.  She loved the silver spoon and the
old clock with its jewel-like pendulum, and she would
fondle the rose-in-glass paperweight as a child would
a doll.  Over Grandma's Passage-of-Time quilts, Molly
went into ecstasies.

These quilts were Grandma's way of keeping a history of the family and friends.  There were twenty-
four blocks to a quilt, each one depicting in appliqué
and embroidery the most interesting events that happened in our lives as time went by.  She drafted her
own designs, for she was good at drawing, and sometimes the completed block would be intricate beyond
all reason and as complicated as a mosaic tile.  Take
the time the bull butted Grandpa into the river and
jumped in after him.  There were three scenes in this
one block—Grandpa standing on the riverbank inno-
cently fishing; Grandpa halfway across the river, the
bull in hot pursuit; and Grandpa climbing a tree on
the other side, water dripping from his clothing in
the form of blue French knots and a satin-stitch blue
jay perched in a tree watching.

Sometimes we chided Grandma about her drawings.
The barn didn't sway in the middle the way ours
really did, and in the block where she had me in the
swing, the tree was generously foliaged and well pro-
portioned instead of a spindly old walnut.

"Well, I draw them like they look to me," Grandma
would say, and that seemed excuse enough.

When relatives gathered, we put these quilts on the
beds for spreads, for they provided no end of fun when
the incidents pictured were recalled.  "Where's that
block of Dad getting the skunks out from under the

floor?" Uncle Hayden would ask and go around from bed to bed until he found it. He'd stand and laugh until the tears rolled down his cheeks and tell the story all over again to anyone near. Grandma always had as many funny blocks as she could.

Molly would feast her eyes for hours at a time on these quilts. "Just seems like if you'd look at pretty things long enough, and handle them often enough, you'd be bound to soak up a little of their beauty, doesn't it?" she would ask pathetically, fingering the mole on her nose.

When work got slack at our house, Molly went on to Staceys', McFarlands', and Ritters'. "You folks have been awful kind," she said when she left. "You don't know how it makes me feel. Almost like it didn't matter so much." We knew she meant her face.

"I guess being kind is the most beautiful thing in the world, and you can't even see it." Molly thought about that for a while and looked sad because you couldn't see such a beautiful thing as kindness. "Maybe that's the kind that you soak up," she added, "the kind you can't see."

After staying a while with all the neighbors, Molly left, and we assumed she had at last saved enough money to have her face "corrected," as she always called it.

She had made sufficient impression, though, to warrant a block in Grandma's quilt. And, as we all liked the funny blocks, we urged Grandma to make one of Molly taking Communion at church with the forgotten pillow pinned over her hips. Molly admired the wasp waists and generous hips of the other ladies, but she was waspy all the way down. Other thin women used discreet padding and crinoline ruffling to make their skirts stand out; but Molly had no time to fix up such trappings for herself and on this particular Sunday she used the simple expedient of a patchwork cushion to correct her figure faults.

"If only she hadn't taken her coat off," deplored the women, who had to listen to much chiding from their menfolk after that. But the old stove in the church had acted up, and Molly, along with many others, took off her coat and marched up the aisle to take Communion, completely oblivious of her "figure correction."

Grandma demurred at making such a block. "Poor, dear girl. I wouldn't poke fun at her for anything," she said. But we continued to insist, assuring Grandma that we'd never hear from Molly Layton again.

But here we had! "Same old Molly," Mrs. Stacey had reported to Grandma over the telephone.

"You mean she didn't get the mole off or the tooth in, as hard as she worked and saved?" Grandma asked.

"No. It seems like a distant cousin of Molly's turned up without any money and needing medicine of some kind. And Molly spent all she had on the cousin getting her straightened out, and didn't have enough left over for herself," Mrs. Stacey said. "Coming back out to go to work again."

And so Grandma was worried. No gift for Molly! Besides, the picture in the quilt!

"I could run her up a little needlecase, I guess," Grandma said, looking at her quilt already stretched in the quilting frame.

We all went out to the kitchen to get the refreshments ready and left Grandma alone while she worked fast on Molly's present.

The house smelled real Christmasy, for we had put the tree up early for the quilting party. Bayberry candles were burning on the mantel, and cinnamon rolls were in the oven. It was snowing softly outside, and the ladies were in a holiday mood as they began arriving.

Molly was the same old Molly, hiding her mouth with her hand when she laughed and hooking her hair behind her ear. If anything, she was even thinner. "When I heard you had another one of those pretty quilts ready," she said to Grandma, "I sure wanted to come along and help work on it."

"Well, we'll start before long," Grandma said, "but first you ladies warm up with a spot of tea." She passed the tea and let me pass the cinnamon rolls and spoons. I saw to it that Molly got the silver spoon. Then Grandma distributed the presents.

There wasn't anything for Molly but an old thimble of Grandma's that had become too large for her. I felt so sorry for Molly, and even sorrier for Grandma, who hadn't had time after all to make anything suitable for Molly.

But Grandma didn't look at all worried. "Molly," she said, "I've put you in the quilt."

A slow blush of pleasure crept up over Molly's face. She threw back her shoulders and took her hand away from her mouth. I followed her to the quilt to see the picture. Wasn't Grandma doing this all wrong? I wondered. Maybe Molly wouldn't have recognized herself. I watched Molly's face closely. She looked a long time at the block. A softness came into her face and then a glow. Why, Molly looked radiant! I peered down at the block. It wasn't the one of Molly with the cushion at all. It was one of Molly putting flowers into a vase. You could tell it was her by the little maid's ruffle she always wore on her head. Grandma had ripped out the other block and substituted this one while we thought she was making the needlecase. I looked at Molly's face again.

Tears were spilling down her cheeks as she lifted her eyes to Grandma's. "But you've made me pretty," she said very softly.

It was true. Grandma had added little lines here and there, and the girl pictured was pretty, but still Molly, all right.

"Well, I just draw them like they look to me," Grandma said.

Somehow, the little thimble Molly had received didn't matter at all. For here, tied in the brightest, shimmering, invisible package, was Grandma's gift to Molly—the kind you couldn't see at all.

## *Good Will Toward Men*

EVERYTHING would have been lovely that Christmas if only the Claytons and the McClanahans would make up and start speaking to each other. Their long-standing feud was an awful bother. You had to remember it even when you had your mind on more pressing matters.

In time of trouble, if Mrs. McClanahan brought us over a cake, we mustn't forget and offer her any of the pie Mrs. Clayton had brought, or vice versa.

When Ladies Aid met, the hostess always had to be careful and show Nettie McClanahan to a chair clear across the room from Bessie Clayton. You couldn't put them on the same committee, of course; and if one voted for, the other automatically voted against.

How the trouble started, no one was quite sure. Some said it was over a line fence way back ten or fifteen years ago. Others said it was over sheep and a dog. Anyway, when the farmers traded work at haying or butchering time, you could be dead sure Coy McClanahan wouldn't show up to help Tom Clayton. Or vice versa.

Like I say, that feud was a bother. But whenever anyone got fed up with it and spoke out in plain

terms, someone also would point out that every community has its McClanahans and Claytons—it's a cross
you have to bear.

Lou was not above using the grudge to advantage.
When she and I sold Ease-All Balm, she'd casually
mention to Nettie McClanahan that Bessie Clayton
had bought three bottles, and we could count on
Nettie's buying four. Or maybe it was the other way
around.

"Maybe it'll ease all between them," Lou said one
day, coming away from such a sale.

"Will it?" I asked eagerly, not being sure just what
the balm was supposed to cure.

"No, it'll take something stronger than this, I'm
afraid." Her brow wrinkled up in that familiar fash-
ion it always had when she was working on a knotty
problem.

"It's pretty strong," I said, opening a bottle and
taking a whiff. When you held it close it made your
eyes turn red and get watery and your nose burn.

The hard feelings might have reached over into the
younger generation of McClanahans and Claytons if
there hadn't been such a difference in ages. McClanahans' Maggie was in the seventh grade with our Lou,
and the Clayton's only child was just four months old.

Lou and I loved to play with Maggie. Besides being pretty—black hair and smutty-fringed blue eyes—
she could sing like there was a thrush in her throat,
make a Jacob's ladder, and whistle through a split
blade of grass. She never talked about the Claytons,
and we never mentioned the trouble either, because
you could see it embarrassed her.

When Lou drew Maggie's name for the Christmas-gift exchange at school, you'd have thought she was planning a present for the First Lady, the way she worried. "I could crochet her a tam," she mused, "but Mrs. Clayton has a tam, so Maggie's mother wouldn't let her wear one."

It was a problem. "You could cross-stitch her a petticoat in the Hearts and Flowers pattern," I offered. But Lou said no, everyone knew she got that pattern from Mrs. Clayton.

Then everything took a back seat while we got ready for the Christmas program. I was a real good reader, so I was assigned the Christmas story to read just before the final tableau. That wouldn't have bothered me, except Lou kept at me to practice "Peace on earth, good will toward men." "That's important," she'd say. "You've got to put *meaning* in it."

You'd have thought Lou herself was preparing for a command performance before royalty, the way she worked on her part of Mary the Mother for the tableau. "I must have blue muslin," she decided, and spent a dreadful sum — all the money she had — for enough to drape herself in. Of course Grandma promised to buy the muslin later for quilt lining.

Lou practiced constantly before the mirror, draping the muslin first one way, then another. She'd nestle the Baby Jesus doll in her right arm, then try the left. Still unsatisfied, she announced dramatically: "I must have a real baby."

Mama protested. "Oh, honey, the doll is all right. A real baby might squall its head off."

"A doll is too stiff," Lou argued. "Anyway, don't

you suppose the Baby Jesus cried sometimes with all those strange people coming to see Him?"

The teacher was skeptical, too, about using a baby; but if you're in doubt as to who won the argument, it's because you didn't know my sister, Lou. The result was that the Claytons' baby was elected. Mrs. Clayton was willing, especially when Lou mentioned that Maggie McClanahan was singing a solo part in "O Come All Ye Faithful."

Lou had invested so heavily in muslin that she couldn't afford to buy Maggie's present. She wound up with a string of blue and yellow beads she made from two old necklaces of Mama's. They were put together real artistically, and Grandma gave her a satin-lined box for them and some holly-sprigged paper.

"While I wrap them, you'd better rehearse the Christmas story," she told me. "You don't have it right yet. When you say 'good will toward men' you've got to make people *feel* it."

"Even the McClanahans and the Claytons?" I asked, and was immediately sorry I'd brought it up because here came that puzzled expression to Lou's face again and I knew she had more important things to think about.

"Even them," she said, slowly, thoughtfully, holding the beads against the muslin of her costume. "These ought to be worn together," she said.

"You wouldn't have the nerve," I said, "to ask Maggie to loan you those beads right after giving them to her."

Lou just stared out the window a long time while the wrinkles in her brow disappeared one by one.

She looked like someone who had turned to the back of the book and found the answer was right.

We had our gift exchange Friday afternoon and Maggie just loved her beads. Lou said, "Be sure and wear them to the program tonight," and Maggie said, "Oh, I will!"

Just before we started for the schoolhouse that night, Lou put a bottle of Ease-All Balm into the pocket of her skirt.

"You going to try to sell some tonight?" I demanded.

She didn't answer, just looked mysterious.

The schoolhouse smelled good and cedary. Red and green crepe paper made a canopy of the ceiling. There were reindeer and evergreen decorations at the windows, and the teacher had erased our demerits from the blackboard. There was a good crowd, too—McClanahans prominent on the left, Claytons on the right as usual.

Everything proceeded nicely until just before the final manger-scene tableau. When Mrs. Clayton brought baby Robert behind the curtain, I got to hold him while Lou unwrapped her Mary costume.

I'd been noticing something odd about Lou. Her eyes were watery and pink-rimmed, and she was sniffling. "Are you crying?" I asked.

She shook her head feebly, pulled out her handkerchief and blew her nose long and hard. "I don't feel so good," she confided. Then, loudly: "I'b taking a nawful gold!"

"So you've got a cold—so what?" said a Wise Man from the East. Lou withered him with a watery glare. "So naturally I can't be Mary and hold that baby in

the tableau," she said firmly. "You want him to catch
cold and be sick?"

Lou could always get attention. Full attention.
Maryellen Britt halted her angel costume halfway over
her head, and the wings stuck up like big ears. The
teacher looked up, startled, from helping Cabe but-
ton his striped-housecoat robe.

"Don't worry," Lou said. "Maggie can be Mary in
my place. All she has to do is hold the baby."

It got real quiet back there then, until finally someone said right out: "It's the Claytons' baby."

We all looked at Maggie and then looked away,
ashamed, when she said quietly: "Why, I'll do it if
the baby's willing."

The teacher stepped in front of the curtain and
announced that for the final number there'd be a slight
change in the cast of characters she'd typed up on the
program. While that was going on, Maggie took her
place on a low stool on stage, and Lou draped the
blue muslin around her. I put the Claytons' baby in
Maggie's arms, and Joseph, in his tow-sack robe, stood
behind them. The choir scurried for position behind
scenes and started humming softly so I could go out
and begin the Christmas story.

I gave "Peace on earth, good will toward men" all
I had, and then our teacher slid back the curtains
while the choir, still muted, sang "Silent Night."

We knew that tableau was a beauty from the
"ohhhhh's" that rippled over the audience. Then a
wave of loud gasps told us that everyone had recognized Maggie McClanahan holding the Claytons' baby.

I looked at Mrs. Clayton and Mrs. McClanahan, and saw them both sit forward in their seats.

Then the baby woke up and started whimpering. His mother made a move like she'd go to his rescue; but Maggie rocked him gently in her arms, and Mrs. Clayton settled back.

About that time the baby reached up and grabbed for Maggie's blue and yellow beads. Maggie bent down and kissed his little hand and didn't pry it away as you'd expect. The choir was singing so low you could hear the baby making gurgly, contented sounds.

Well, Lou's cold couldn't hold a candle to the one that hit the audience right then! You could hear noses blowing all over the schoolroom.

No one clapped when the tableau was over because it was too beautiful and sacred. Instead, people turned to each other and started shaking hands like they hadn't seen each other since the last Christmas.

When I took Mrs. Clayton's baby to her, Mrs. McClanahan was standing close by. "Here, let me hold that little thing," she said, and Mrs. Clayton let her. And when Maggie came to get her hair ribbon tied back on, Mrs. Clayton said, "Let me do that."

Back near the door Mr. Clayton was holding out his hand to Mr. McClanahan, or maybe it was vice versa.

When Lou came out from backstage, Mama felt her forehead and looked puzzled. She didn't dope my sister's cold that night with a greasy flannel rag; but next day Lou got to wear Grandma's ring and Mama's rouge, and I heard them plotting to make her a ruffled petticoat from Mary's robe. She got to eat with the silver spoon throughout the holidays.

And that's not all. On Christmas Eve Mrs. Clayton came over with some cookies and sailed right into a piece of the pie that Mama specifically said Mrs. Mc-Clanahan had brought. Or maybe it was vice versa.

# Christmas Cooking

THE KITCHEN was the hub of our lives. From it we went forth, and to it we returned. The front door was used only by strangers—or when it was known that Mama and Grandma were having Ladies Aid. The kitchen was big enough (once it had been a single-room log-cabin home) for one to carry on an industry of dressmaking, or reading, at one end, completely undisturbed by the rest of the activity going on, yet be pleasantly aware of the nearness of loved ones and the hum of homey occupations.

How pleasant it was on gloomy, dark winter days after the long, cold walk home from school to come into its warmth! Rain dripped off the low eaves and made a cozy patter on the pantry roof. Old Tabby, curled up on the hearth, purred loudly, loving the stir of our homecoming and the good smells emanating from the oven. The teakettle on the back of the stove sang gaily and every once in a while a log in the fireplace would break in two, causing a busy sputtering of sparks.

Many of our treasures were concentrated in this one room where we could look around and see them all at once. There was the clock on the mantel with its exquisite jewel-like pendulum, the big hunk of many-faceted green glass that was used as a doorstop, the colorful Mexican basket hanging on the wall, and the Blue Willow bean jar on the cabinet. The walls were decorated with such necessary items as the almanac, the shaving mirror and comb rack, and a map of Europe. The continent of Europe was changing. Mama had marked with a pencil the location of the Marne River where her Cousin Jim had recently been killed. There was a huge bird chart we'd gotten with carefully saved Arm and Hammer baking soda cards. Winter birds, summer birds, meadow birds, mountain birds were all assembled in one setting, and the purple grackle had an insect in its mouth.

The big square table in the center of the room wasn't merely a place to eat. It doubled as Mama's cutting board when she sewed. It was our study table. There we played checkers and dominoes and a most peculiar game that I have never seen repeated by other children. It originated in the fertile brain of Lou, and had it been named it would probably have been called "Salting the Heifers." This game was best indulged in when Mama and Grandma and all other adults were outside. A small pile of salt was spooned onto the corners of the table. Then we pursued each other around the table, having to stop at each corner and take a lick at the salt with our tongues. What hilarious fun to see the pained expressions on each other's faces when we had reached the saturation point of salt consumption. Of course the floor became good and crunchy, too, and ofttimes, if it were summer when we played barefooted and there happened to be a raw, sore toe, one participant might be sent yelling for the wash pan, where the offended member was quickly dipped.

But it was at Christmas time that the kitchen really came into its own. Although there was much good cooking going on at other seasons throughout the year, especially at threshing time or any summer Sunday when company was expected, still it was at Christmas that it was most enjoyed, for the heat from the old black range was welcome and comforting then.

We seldom had company for Christmas dinner on account of the roads. By this time frozen ruts were so deep and continuous that it was a cold, hazardous journey for the aunts and uncles and cousins. If the neighbors dropped in, they walked, and we would serve them hot buttered popcorn or a plate of molasses candy. But still we baked and fried and stewed and boiled from a week before Christmas clear up through New Year's, experimenting with new recipes and perfecting the old ones.

Throughout the holidays, everyone's favorite cake, cookie, or pie would be served, so the route to the cellar, the smokehouse, and pantry, that great triumvirate for the garnishment of our table, was kept well traversed. There was a constant warm smell of vanilla, cinnamon, nutmeg, rising dough, roasting meat, baking bread, and boiling cranberries. We picked out quarts of hickory nuts and walnut kernels and shelled gallons of popcorn.

Starting off early in the holidays with the plebeian gingerbread, butter, molasses, and ginger cookies, we progressed through raisin, mincemeat, and pumpkin pies; raised doughnuts fried in the deep leaf lard in the old three-legged kettle; pound cake, devil's cake, hickory-nut cake, divinity, and fudge, to wind up with the glorious queens of all, Grandma's five-layer cocoanut cake and Mama's peach custard pudding.

Of course, in and out and round about all these sweetenings were the rosy, pink slices of baked ham; the pungent brown sausages replete with salt, pepper, and plenty of sage; golden, bubbly chicken pie, butter beans, green beans, pinto beans; fried, baked, boiled and scalloped potatoes; cole slaw, and a roster of pickles and jellies that would reach from one end of the valley to the other.

But on Christmas Day, there for dinner, centering the table on the glass-stemmed stand, was the high, light, creamy, five-layer, becocoanutted cake, and for supper the golden-studded, meringue-covered peach custard pudding.

Grandma had three, little, thin, tin cake pans which she kept on top of the pantry shelves for her cake-baking alone. Woe be to anyone who dared to use them for anything else. In preparation for her cake baking she washed and dried these carefully, greased and floured them lightly, and distributed them equally distant along the top of the cook table. There was nothing slipshod or bang-up about this culinary concoction.

Lou and I, who have seen to it that the wood box is filled and spilling over with good dry split wood, pulled from underneath the pile, are allowed to lean our elbows on the table and watch the proceedings.

Into the big blue crock Grandma drops a cup of

butter, and over this she sifts a cup of sugar. Then, with the big cooking spoon, she whips and beats, mashes, spins and cajoles it into a light, fluffy mass, the color of the creamy white honeysuckles on the summer porch. At this point on lesser occasions she would poke a spoonful of the sugary concoction into two drooling mouths, but not today!

Then come the eggs, five or six, broken deftly on the edge of the crock and spilled over the contents. Then again the beating process, even more vigorous than before. The withered skin at Grandma's throat flaps back and forth, and her old hand, gnarled from too much rheumatism, goes round so fast it is just a blur. The rickrack on her dust cap quivers and the batter grows lighter and lighter. Grandma does not measure her flour but grabs the sifter, puts in a certain amount of baking powder and salt, just so much flour, and proceeds to raise a fine white mist in, over, and around the cook table. Flour, milk, flour, milk, until the right consistency is reached—and only she knows this—then the vanilla, more beating, and into the three pans. That's all the oven will hold at one time. After the first baking, two of the pans are pressed into the second shift.

How the cake eventually comes out even and well rounded is a feat architectural more than culinary because the layers are invariably higher on one side than the other. This is due to the fact that the whole kitchen slopes a little downhill toward the river. But by alternating the high and low sides, putting a bigger daub of icing here, a smaller amount of cocoanut there, it goes upwards, plumb with the table, pleasing to the eye, and perfect to the palate.

After feasting our eyes on it the remainder of the morning, sitting in all its chaste glory in the center of the white-covered table and coming into even more tantalizing proximity during the meal, finally Grandpa would cross his knife and spoon neatly on his plate, pick up crumbs, real and imaginary, and after an eternity say, "Now, Ma, give me a slice of the riverward side of that cake."

It was inconceivable that when only a third of the ambrosial mass remained, leaning precariously like Pisa, that we would ever again want anything to eat, especially so soon as suppertime. But appetites would be whetted by coasting down the hill back of the house, skating on the frozen river, or merely by taking a long tramp in the snow, to say nothing of the evening chores that would come later.

Taking a long tramp over the farm was Grandpa's favorite way of spending a Christmas afternoon. Sort of a busman's holiday since he had spent a good part of the spring, summer, and fall walking over the farm, but this day he set aside to check up on his little animals, as he called all the furry creatures that made their homes up and down the river valley.

Chances were Lou and I had found some new red knitted mittens and sock caps under the Christmas tree that morning, so, donning these, coats, and galoshes, we accompanied Grandpa on the trip.

He was a stern taskmaster in the matter of local animal lore. You couldn't really get a good grasp on things, he maintained, unless you knew the life that went on about you in the fields and woods. "It'd be just like getting a new suit and never putting your hands in any of the pockets," he explained.

He spat in disgust when we confused the tracks of the possum with those of the coon and, I believe, he would have rapped us on the head had we mistaken the way the rabbit was going from his footprints in the snow.

So we came to look upon the little animals as a part of the farm and felt secretly rich and inordinately proud when we found the hollow-tree home of some smelly skunk or knew where the possum had a nest of young. "You know the possums are no bigger than a pinto bean when they're born, don't you?" Grandpa demanded, which was his way of telling us, and, although we didn't know, we never forgot thereafter.

We knew at what hour to find the muskrat sunning on his sycamore snag, tracked hundreds of rabbits to their briar patches, and even found the mud slide of an otter once.

Adding something tangible to our knowledge, like finding a quail nest or a fox den, was just like having a new possession, and we weren't above bragging about it at school and elsewhere and using it for trading timber. Once I had canceled a debt of twenty-five sheets of slick tablet paper I owed for showing someone a chipmunk's burrow.

We even felt proprietary towards old "P.B.," the terrapin, although it was our neighbor, Paul Britt, who had carved his initials on the shell long ago. But he was found mostly on our place, poking his inquisitive head up among the dewberry vines, giving us a terrible start, or resting under a May apple umbrella. Then maybe in less than a week we'd run across him in the bluebells, way over in the far meadow. Sometimes a year would go by before we'd hear from him, then one night at supper Grandpa would report, "Ran across old P.B. today." It was like hearing from an old friend. We were interested in his perambulations.

So, on such a Christmas Day, if we were blessed with snow, we might find the dainty handprints of the mink, the larger ones of the coon and possum, the triangular tracks of the rabbit, and the delicate embroidery stitches of the field mice.

"Un-huh," Grandpa would say, satisfactorily, when he came across them, and looking on, Lou and I had the feeling that all was going well. Running ahead to a smooth, snow-deep place in the meadow, we would lie flat on our backs, sweep our arms in semicircles, making "angel" tracks of our own, and wait to see what Grandpa would do when he came across them. "And this," he'd say in heavy reverence, "is where the angels slept last night!"

December twilight came on fast. At the hour of four we began to close the day. Long since the icicles had ceased to drip and begun to grow thick and lengthy again, making a pretty fringe at the barn's eaves and around the roof of the chicken house.

There is warmth and life in the barn. Shaggy-haired cows low gently at the sound of milk buckets rattling, and horses make soft throaty sounds through their velvet nostrils. Barn cats crouch close to some convenient mouse hole that leads to hidden rooms within rooms where beady-eyed creatures make noises with

favorite old corncobs and leave intricate patterns on
the dusty floor. Up in the cavernous region of the
rafters are the mud daubers' labyrinthine homes, and
woolly spiders hang their winter festoons across the
gable windows.

The wind whistles around the corners, sifting snow
about, and through it we see the lights from the
kitchen where warmth and food await. For supper
there are the dinner leftovers, plus the peach custard
pudding. For this delectable dessert, Mama has put
cookie crumbs in the bottom of the big corn-bread
pan, poured on melted butter, and arranged peach
halves in symmetrical rows. This is all buried under
a cream custard and topped with nubby meringue,
browned to golden perfection in the oven, and served
generously in the gold-rimmed glass dessert dishes.

After supper we will go over our presents again.
Perhaps Uncle Hayden has sent us some new records
for the gramaphone—"The Preacher and the Bear," or
"Moonlight in Jungleland," and we play them over
and over. Lou and I fondle our gifts, a big red lady-
bug that winds up and crawls across the floor, some
doll dresses, a scrapbook Lillian has prepared for us,
flannelette and serge to go into winter clothes, and
the big, rare oranges we keep laying aside, saving the
best for the last.

"Fill'er up again?" Dad asks, lifting the stove lid
to one side and peering in.

Grandma yawns and reckons she's ready to turn
in. We are not reluctant to follow suit for it has been
a good day, and there is tomorrow and tomorrow and
tomorrow.

## *Winter Visitor*

O**N A COLD** winter night when snow lay drifted in knee-deep banks and sleet rattled bleakly against the windowpanes, there came a sudden knock at our door.

It was not a timid, hesitant, halfhearted knock, which, half waking, one would think was only the loose shutter or the maple limb that rubbed against the house, but a bold, decisive, imperative knocking, one that brought the family bolt upright in bed with no intermediate stage between sleep and wakefulness.

We weren't scared. My, no. We all had separate plans and devices to foil a criminal should ever one have the nerve or misfortune to stumble onto our premises. Sometimes, when we read in the *Farmington News* about burglars and thieves in faraway places, we—at least Lou and I—secretly wished one would come along so we could test some of our plans. There were five hound dogs and one shepherd to sick on the culprit, cans of Merry War lye on the pantry shelves to open and toss about, a big, quilt-sized minnow seine in the smokehouse to entangle him, the loose shutter upstairs to throw down, and somewhere, though heavens knew where, a rusty old gun.

No, we weren't scared by the sudden knocking, way past midnight. Just curious. Whoever would be caught out a night like this? And here, so far away from anyplace? Even our nearest neighbor we hadn't seen for a month, and probably wouldn't until this current snow disappeared that had us so thoroughly bound in. The only sign of outward human life we had seen recently had been the smoke from the train that ran through the valley.

Out of the bedrooms and down the stairs we poured, Grandpa and Dad pulling on their moleskins over long underwear, Mom and Grandma getting into robes, and we girls holding up long flannelette nightgowns.

"Now it's the front door," Grandpa said, in an organizational voice, holding aloft the lamp and halting us at the foot of the stairs while we arranged ourselves in a semblance of order as we were always prone to do in situations that demanded a united front. Grandpa and Dad were first, with Grandma and Mom close behind, and Lillian, Lou, and I came trailing out singly like the knotted tail of a kite.

Bringing up the rear as I did, I didn't always get a good look at what was going on up front, but I could hear, and when things sounded all right it was my privilege, as the last knot on the kite string, to whip around quickly from side to side and observe.

Having heard Grandpa open the front door and greet the stranger with no accompanying dull, sickening thuds on the head, I peeped around from behind the array of voluminous nightgowns and robes and saw the handsome stranger. He was clad in a black

Chesterfield coat like our Uncle Hayden had. In one hand, having just removed it, was a gray felt hat. In the other he carried a black valise. The snow, blowing through the open doorway, was catching and holding on his silver-trimmed black hair. The lamplight caught the fine sparkle in his dark eyes and glistened on his white, chattering teeth.

"Kind people," he addressed the assemblage with a low bow, "it has been my misfortune to become lost in this monstrous snowstorm. It is with the deepest regret that I have called you from your warm beds to the door. Had I been able to find shelter of the humblest sort, I would not have thought of disturbing you, and even would have continued to brave the elements had I not feared the circulation in my hands and feet were slowing to a stop."

"He's freezing to death," Grandma quickly translated. "Come in and shut the door," she commanded, bustling around, tying an apron on over her robe. "Steve, stir up the fire. Put the coffee on, someone."

"Oh, pray, make no trouble for me," the stranger said, lifting a blue-cold staying hand. "Just let me sit here inside the door until morning. I shall be quiet, so as not to disturb your sleep further. When it is dawn, I shall depart and be forever grateful."

"Where you from?" Grandpa asked, opening the top of the chunk stove and stirring up the coals.

"Fortunate it is that I am to stumble in this Stygian blackness onto such hospitable people," the stranger went on. "I tell you, the likes of you are seldom seen these days. Madam," he turned to Grandma, "a drink of warm water would be sufficient."

"Warm water, pshaw," Grandma snorted.

"Where you bound for?" Dad asked, pulling a chair up to the stove for the stranger.

"I was just saying to myself," the man continued, "if I do not find shelter in the next half hour, I shall just lie down in a snowbank and let come what may. It would not be such a bad way out of life's furnace of living. And I was counting off the seconds when your blessed door loomed up in front of me. Won't you little girls return to your beds?" He flashed his fullest smile on the three of us, sitting on the edge of the divan, and quite melted our hearts.

"Give him our bed," Lou blurted out in a fit of compassion.

"Oh, no, no, no," he protested. "Just here on the floor by the stove will be like a king's bedchamber to me."

"Pshaw," Grandma reiterated from the closet, bringing out the white wool blanket, the flower-garden quilt, the embroidered pillowcases, and the company sheets we kept stored in lavender. A bed was made on the divan, and after our guest had drunk three or four cups of steaming coffee, the family retired to their cold rooms, leaving the stranger to the warmth of the living room and the lavender-scented bed.

"Who is he?" Mom asked Dad as we made our way back up the stairs.

"He didn't say," Dad replied, scratching his cheek slowly.

"Well, he didn't, did he?" Mom remarked, somewhat surprised. "But then, he didn't ask who we were either, did he?" She laughed softly at the strange state of affairs.

Lou and I snuggled down in bed again and talked far into what was left of the night. "He was a fine-looking gentleman, wasn't he? Didn't he talk different, though? Going to sleep in a snowbank to escape the 'furnace of living'? Did you see the great diamond ring on his finger? Maybe he's a minister, or a doctor. Wonder where he came from? He didn't say, did he?" We drifted off to sleep, contented and pleasantly excited, for there would be something different on the morrow, a stranger in the house to relieve the monotony of our snowbound days.

At breakfast we acted like we were accustomed to the tablecloth and napkins and the best dishes. There was the last jar of strawberry preserves, which we knew Mom had been saving for an occasion. So, this was it! We, accordingly, ate with one hand in our laps, elbows in, knife across plate, please pass, and thank you.

"Nothing like winter in the country to whet one's appetite," the stranger commented, taking a second helping of ham. "Beautiful place you have here. Picturesque. Although somewhat remote, I take it. You don't have many visitors, do you?"

"We haven't seen anyone for a month," Lou volunteered.

The stranger looked pleased, like he was embarking on a new adventure. "And I suppose you don't go anywhere much?"

"We don't even go to school hardly now," I told him.

Mom gave Lou and me a look that suggested the

stranger might like to carry on a bit of conversation with the adults.

"Suppose a person did wish to leave, how would be the quickest way out?" he asked.

"How did you get in?" Grandpa countered pleasantly.

"Ah, yes, I neglected to tell you that story, didn't I? I was riding the train that goes through here somewhere and they let me off at the wrong place." He laughed at the big joke and we all laughed with him.

"Well, in a way it was my fault," he explained. "I thought it was Bismarck we were whistling for. Asked the person in the seat next to me and he said it was, so I just got off." He shrugged his shoulders and turned up his palms at the simplicity of it. "Snowing so hard I couldn't tell right off that it wasn't a town."

"And you wallowed all the way up the tracks through this snow to our place?" Mom marveled.

"Seems like a meant thing, doesn't it?" the stranger agreed, looking sober.

Dad and Grandpa got ready to leave the house to feed the cattle.

"Could I help you, sirs?" the stranger begged, thus relieving the hesitancy Grandpa and Dad seemed to have about both leaving the house at the same time.

"You're hardly dressed for it," Grandpa commented, buckling on his high felt boots and turning up the collar of his Mackinaw.

"That's right," the stranger laughed, pulling up his trousers to reveal low-cut shoes. "Well, perhaps there is something I can do here at the house to repay you for my night's lodging."

The family protested in unison.

"We all just kind of live here in the kitchen of mornings," Mom explained apologetically, after Dad and Grandpa left.

"An utterly charming place it is," the stranger complimented. He walked around, looking at the bird chart, the old clock, the crocheted shawl over the back of the hickory rocker. "Someone here has studied interior decorating or else one has the gifted hand of an artist."

Mom blushed and Grandma dropped a fork, and into the pleasant silence that followed, I asked, "Do you play checkers?"

"Why, of course, I play checkers." He tousled my hair kindly.

"Jeanie!" Mom said, half scolding.

"It's all right, madam. I'll count it a pleasure to entertain the children. Come, let us sit here by the window and have a game."

"It's cold by the window," I told him.

"But, it's so nice to look out. See, the snow has put white turbans on the fence posts to keep their heads warm. And the telephone line looks as if—" He stopped suddenly and went quickly to the telephone, lifted the receiver, and listened.

"Law me, I guess the line is down in half a dozen places," Mom said.

"Yes, of course," he smiled and took his chair by the window. "Now, let's sit here and watch the people go by." He laughed and we all laughed with him. It was good to have someone different around.

During the game he kept looking at the road as if he really expected people to be coming and going.

When Dad returned from the barn, he came over to where we were playing, without even taking his coat and boots off, and said, "I don't believe you told us your name, sir."

The man made a sudden poor play and I jumped three of his men. Then he turned to Dad. "Oh, so I didn't. Funny how elementary things escape us when caught in the grip of great forces of nature. I was just saying—"

"My name is Bell," Dad interrupted, offering his hand.

"My name is Checkers," the stranger said. He rose and shook hands with Dad very formally.

Lou and I started giggling. "Isn't it funny? We were just playing checkers, and his name is Checkers?" I marveled.

"A coincidence," Dad remarked.

"I spell it with an *S*," the stranger explained. "Sheckers."

Shucks, it wasn't so funny after all.

"We've got an old sleigh down at the barn," Dad said. "If you're of a mind to leave, I think we could get you down to the train stop again."

"Oh, pray, sir, I wouldn't trouble you so. I'll just bundle up and leave as I came and be forever grateful for you kind people. Would have left this morning as I planned, but I thought the snow might stop by afternoon. Perhaps it will."

By afternoon, Mr. Sheckers was sick. It started with a flushing of his face and then he had a chill right over the stove with two wool blankets wrapped around him. Grandma laid a hand on his forehead and clucked her tongue dismally.

It was a sort of three-day kind of flu for which we were all thankful. To have gotten a doctor out from town would have been next to impossible on account of the roads, though Dad offered to try to go after one.

"No, no, no." Mr. Sheckers was almost cross in his protestations and got up out of bed as if to prevent any such actions.

Grandma made her special soup for sick people and Mama gave the patient our own brand of cough medicine out of the silver spoon. Lou and I, looking on, shuddered for poor Mr. Sheckers.

"A lovely spoon," he commented, taking it from Mom's hand and inspecting it, turning it over to see the label on the back. "Do you have a whole set?"

"No," Mama said.

"We get to take medicine out of it, too, when we're sick," I told him.

"Where do you keep the rest of them?" he asked.

Mama looked at him in surprise as if it were a peculiar question.

"Well, I mean," Mr. Sheckers faltered, "you don't eat with them every day, do you? If a person has anything lovely, it should be used all the time, I think."

"We only have the one," Mama explained.

When Mr. Sheckers was able to come to the table again, Grandpa started off the conversation in a hearty manner. "Headed for Bismarck, were you? Got folks there?"

"Yes, sir."

"What's their name? May know them."

"Henshaw," Mr. Sheckers said. He looked around the table to see if any of us brightened with recognition. "Aunt Mabel and Uncle Tom," he added. "Haven't seen them in years."

Lou and I wished that Mr. Sheckers would be snowbound with us all winter. He knew different games, could tell stories and recite poetry. One afternoon, when Dad and Grandpa were out, Lou and I begged him to do "The Highwayman" again for us. He could make us cry every time.

"I like you," I told him frankly, blinking through my tears when he had finished.

There came a funny, faraway look into his eyes. He laid his hand on my head, started to say something, and didn't. He walked over to the window and looked out a long, long time. He held his hands together behind him so tightly that the knuckles turned white. Suddenly he faced about from the window. "I tell you what," he said brightly. "Let's have a tea party."

"A tea party," Mom said softly, almost reverently.

"A tea party," the rest of us echoed.

"I'll get the tea," Grandma said, practically, hurrying to the pantry.

"Do you have a lace cloth?" Mr. Sheckers asked, helping to clear the kitchen table.

"Oh, no," Mom said sadly, like it was all off.

"No matter, no matter." He brushed it aside as a picayune.

"A linen one," Mom suggested.

"Fine, fine," he said. "Now, sugar, spoons, and cups."

Lou and I flew to the cabinet to get the cups and set them around the table.

"Oh, no, no, no," he protested. "You set the cups at one end—like this. Then someone sits here and pours the tea from a pot as you line up and come around."

Our faces fell.

"What's the matter?" he demanded.

"No teapot." Grandma stated our dilemma. "Just a coffeepot."

"Oh, that's where I come in. I happen to have one here in my valise. A little present I was taking to Aunt Mabel. We'll just use it."

He took his valise off into the front room to open it, and came back in a minute with the teapot. It was the prettiest thing any of us had ever seen. Squatty at the bottom and growing slender toward the top, a spout as graceful as a swallow's wing and a handle with little curlicues. It was silver, polished and gleaming, intricately engraved.

We stood in awed silence as we always did in the presence of something perfect and beautiful.

"Now, who will sit here and pour?" he asked.

"We'll take turns," Mom suggested.

Oh, it was fun. We didn't sit at the table but just around the room anywhere, as Mr. Sheckers taught us to do. We tried to hold the old kitchen cups like they were fine china, and the tea tasted ever so good.

When it was my turn to pour, my hands were shaking so I almost missed the cups. I ran my hand lovingly over the silver teapot and looked closely at the engraving. It seemed like the bird and feather writing our Uncle Hayden could do. Why, here was a name on the side. I spelled it out to myself. "It says 'Caroline,' on it," I exclaimed.

Mr. Sheckers set his cup down noisily. "Yes," he explained. "Most people call my Aunt Mabel by her second name, 'Caroline.' "

We cleared it all away before Dad and Grandpa got back from the barn and it was a sort of unspoken agreement that we would not mention it. It would seem a bit frivolous, drinking tea from a silver teapot while they were out in the freezing weather, feeding pigs and bedding down cattle.

After supper that day, Grandpa said he believed he'd try to get over to the mailbox on the morrow.

Mr. Sheckers looked up quickly, "I'll go with you," he suggested.

"Oh, no need," Grandpa replied.

"I'll go for you, then," Mr. Sheckers amended. "Where is the mailbox?"

"Oh, Steve," Grandma put in, "probably won't be anything there but the *Farmington News* and I guess it can wait another week."

Grandpa made no answer. We popped corn, ate apples, and went to bed.

The next morning Mr. Sheckers was gone. There was no trace of him whatsoever, except his footprints leading away from the back door.

"Well, better go after him," Dad said. "He's likely to get lost again."

"Oh, let him go," Mom protested. "If he wanted to leave like this, it would only embarrass him to be caught."

"Peculiar fellow," Dad said, and Grandpa nodded his head in agreement.

We womenfolk didn't see anything wrong with him. In fact, Lou and I had such long faces after his departure that Mom, trying to cheer us, said that as soon as the snow melted, we could give a tea party and invite some of the neighbors, now that we knew the proper way to conduct one.

It snowed off and on for four more days. Grandpa didn't go after the mail for another week. We had lots of it when he did go. Mom's magazine had come. There were sale circulars for Lillian, Lou, and me to study, and a new wallpaper book from which to contemplate homemade valentines. We settled down to reading it all after supper that day.

"Been a burglary in at the county seat," Grandpa said, turning the pages of the paper.

"Did they catch him?" I asked.

"He walked in and confessed," Grandpa said, after reading on a while. "Had a whole valise full of stolen stuff. Candlesticks, teapots, jewelry." He started reading aloud to us, " 'The criminal said he had gotten entangled in the furnace of living because he had become convinced that there was no longer any human kindness and compassion and decency in this world. However, a recent experience, the criminal said, had caused him to think otherwise and he wished to start life anew after he had paid his social debt.' "

Mom dropped her magazine and looked at Dad, and Grandma stopped knitting. "Does it give his name?" she demanded interestedly.

"Elam Hagarty," Grandpa read. "Of course, he used

lots of other names. Used to be a schoolteacher, it says."

"I just wish a burglar would come around here," Lou said, a menacing look coming into her eyes. "I'd pour boiling water out the upstairs window on him."

"I'd gig him with the gig," I vouched.

"I'd stick him with the pitchfork." Lou's voice grew more determined.

"I'd cut his head off with the sickle," I said, going all out.

"Children, children," Mom scolded, putting an end to our gruesome plans. "Sometimes a little human kindness and decency works wonders. Look what it did for Mr. Hagarty? Besides, I'm not sure you'd know a burglar when you saw one, nor would I." She laughed. She and Dad and Grandma and Grandpa exchanged peculiar knowing glances and we all went back to our reading.

"Jeanie, see if the silver spoon is in the drawer," Mom said after a while.

This seemed funny to me since no one had to take any medicine that night.

"It's there," I reported.

"All right," Mom said, going back to her reading.

The sleet peppered against the windowpanes. Upstairs the loose shutter rattled softly. The teakettle made contented sounds on the back of the stove. Old Tabby purred on the hearth. After a while Grandma got up and set the buckwheat cakes to rise for breakfast and we all went to bed.

# The Days Go By

G OT A calendar today," Grandpa announces. *A calendar!* Next it will be, "Heard frogs last night." "Here's the sassafras roots." "Saw a robin today." And so on through the year. But a calendar! It means that now everything will be to do all over again. However, we are a year older and a year wiser, and this year we will do everything a little better. The rhubarb does not do well on that side of the garden, so it will be moved. The Home Demonstration agent has taught us how to can pork. The mixture of laying mash Grandpa and Dad have concocted produces more eggs. We have learned from our neighbors, made new friends, experienced and observed, formed new opinions, and strengthened old convictions. Lou has grown into Lillian's clothes and I into Lou's. This might be the year all the cows will have twin calves and the hens will lay in December as they did in May.

But, first things first—the INTEREST, on or before the fifteenth of January! Sometimes the corn did it. Other times the wheat, or the two combined. Maybe a fat steer or two. Always we try to do it without having to sell any of the A.T. & T. stock.

When the subject is brought out in the open, usually at the supper table so that every member of the family will have a knowledge of the running affairs of the farm, Lou, never one to mince or pussyfoot around a vital issue, asks flat out, "Are we gonna have enough without selling the A.T. & T.?"

Lou and I didn't even know we had such stock until we came to that chapter in arithmetic concerning stocks and bonds.

In order to explain the workings of such mysterious things, the teacher asked if we knew whether any of our folks had any stocks and bonds. To our amazement, the Russells said they were quite sure that their uncle had some General Electric stock and the McFarlands had heard of A.T. & T., which the teacher explained to us meant American Telephone and Telegraph.

On our way home from school Lou and I discussed the matter of investments further, arriving at the conclusion we didn't have any.

"I guess we're poor," Lou said, shaking her head sadly.

"I guess so," I agreed.

We did our best to feel forlorn about this condition, but thinking of the good warm supper that awaited us, the comfort of the old kitchen, and the fact that we'd all be there as usual, we just didn't feel poor.

That night, as we sat at the table working our arithmetic problems, Lou announced to the rest of the family that the Russells had kinfolks who owned stocks and bonds.

"Well, that's nice," Mama said, going on with her patching.

"Some of the McFarlands have A.T. & T., too," Lou added.

No further comment was made. After a while, Grandpa, having finished reading the paper, put his glasses away, stretched, and said, "Well, I guess I better see about our own A.T. & T. stock."

"We got A.T. & T.?" Lou asked eagerly. We didn't think Grandpa had even been listening.

Grandpa looked at Mom as if seeking for permission to reveal the truth of this news.

"Why, of course, we got A.T. & T.," Mama confirmed, laughing.

On the morning of Interest Paying Day the roosters seem to crow a little louder. Old Anabelle, Trudy, and Trixy clang their bells and snort and blow bran around in their feedboxes, wanting everyone to know they have a hand in this, too. Grandpa strops his razor noisily in preparation for his trip to the bank. Grandma says she believes she'll just stir up a cake. Lou and I polish our shoes and put on our second-best dresses.

"My, what are you two dressed up about today?" they ask at school.

"Oh, Vermont declared its independence on this day in 1777," Lou replies airily, leaving eyebrows raised all around. It said that on our new calendar Grandpa hung up by the comb rack.

"And it's Jean Baptiste Poquelin's birthday," I add for good measure.

"You got a piece of his birthday cake?" Anna Kotiski asks, looking speculatively at my lunch box.

"Fried cakes," I reply.

Anna sighs in deep satisfaction and I hope Mama has put in several cakes, and more than likely she has for today is Interest Paying Day.

Winter days wear on. Grandpa takes new straw to the hound-dog pens. Tabby and Tom sleep all day in the attic and at night we open the attic door and invite them to sleep on the foot of our bed. Humped-up rabbits make short tours over the resting garden. New snow comes on top of old.

On Saturdays, if it is not too utterly cold in the attic, we play there a while, going through the old trunks, dressing ourselves and Tom and Tabby, looking at old pictures and old valentines. *Valentines!* Hurriedly we repack the trunks, gather bits of old wallpaper, discarded flower catalogues, crayons, scissors and paste, and set up shop in front of the kitchen fireplace. Old store-boughten valentines are cut up, rearranged, and pasted together anew. Bits of lace and red satin, cotton-padded hearts, sprinkled inside with our Christmas talcum powder, are pressed into use. I do not dare to cut out the phrase, "I love you" and paste it on my valentines, so Lou uses them all, sending such sentiments promiscuously to Ercle, Lee-mon, Medford and a half dozen others. My prettiest one I choose for Cabe Ashton.

When the valentines are done and still the long day is not over, Mama says we might have a baking spree since the oven is hot. Lou works with the gingerbread dough making nothing so common as a gingerbread man, but likenesses of Britt's bull, old Jethro; the hound; and snakes, zigzagged snakes with swollen stomachs, tapering tails, and bulgy, raisin eyes. The tails, being thin, were always burnt a little and we had to break them off, but who wanted to eat the rattle anyway!

With the oven filled with doughy animals I rack my brains for top-of-the-stove cookery. Examination of the wooden bread mixing bowl reveals a leftover wad of dough from the morning's biscuits. This I roll out with much deliberation and many times. I have all afternoon and to me the texture never mattered. Cut into varied shapes, I not being as talented as Lou, and fried in the big black pot, then rolled in sugar and cinnamon, they were tasty to me and the family ate them gallantly, along with the gingerbread bulls and snakes.

It is dark in the kitchen on gray winter days. So Mama and Grandma do what they can to better the situation. Across one window sets the big majestic cabinet. Clear up to the ceiling it reaches, replete with flour bin, meal bin, concealed breadboard, spice shelves, dish shelves, and several drawers for countless other things. There seems no other proper place for the cabinet except across the window, for here it is handy to the pantry and the cookstove.

"Can't we knock out this part?" Mama asks, pointing to the back portion from the working top up to the first shelves. "Then the window would show through."

"Why, of course," Grandma exclaims, provoked because we haven't thought of it before.

With claw hammer, chisel and saws, she and Mama remove the portion that has obstructed the light from the lower panes of the window. Now there is light to work by, and, sitting down, we can see clear out to the cellar door and the cherry tree and the clothes line. What a wonderful place for red geraniums!

When Mrs. Kotiski came to see us, she couldn't get over our cabinet.

"Before this, I never saw a like one," she declared, standing off a proper distance to admire it.

"Well, it's just an ordinary cabinet," Mama said.

"No, no," Mrs. Kotiski protested. "Never is one like this in whole world." There is awe in her voice.

We looked at it critically after that and for the life of us couldn't see how it was any different from those other housewives had for miles around. Just a plain, ordinary, stained-oak cabinet with a piece of linoleum on the top.

But Mrs. Kotiski continued to admire it inordinately every time she came, and later, when we decided to get one of the new white ones coming out, Mama said she was just going to give the old one to Mrs. Kotiski, so she had Dad and Grandpa haul it over to her cabin.

If Mrs. Kotiski had admired our old one, we wondered what she would think of our wonderful new white one. We couldn't help but feel a little surprised when she gave it no more than passing notice.

We asked her how she liked the one we had given her, now that she had it up in her own kitchen.

"Is fine," she replied, but gone was the enthusiasm,

the light in her eyes she had had heretofore when speaking of it.

When the Kotiskis decided to move on, seeking greener pastures, we were surprised to see Mr. Kotiski coming up the road with our old cabinet in the back of the wagon. Mrs. Kotiski was with him. They were bringing the cabinet back!

"Is too big for us to move around," she explained, "and, anyway, is not so nice after out you took the window."

"Window?" Mom questioned.

"Yes," Mrs. Kotiski replied, sadly. "For you it had a window."

After that we moved the shiny new cabinet over to the other side of the kitchen and put the old one right back where it belonged, where its "window" let in the light and kept the geraniums blooming, and, through the years, whenever we were unable to see any particular beauty or merit in anything, we were very tolerant for, after all, maybe someone else could see a window in it.

# Whittlin' Man

ON WINTER evenings a frequent visitor around our fireplace was Jeem Hollister. Jeem lived at Laurel Cove, far up the mountain where the mists were last to disappear of a morning and where his cabin remained in sunlight long after the evening shadows had crept over the valley below. He lived all alone, which was unnatural for a man his age—twenty-eight. Not to mention such other features as his quiet eyes, dark hair, and handsome ruggedness.

Jeem had been to the wars and while he was gone his mother and father had died and his girl, Ginny Crawford, had up and married another man. So no one expected him to come back and stay on his scrubby, honeysuckle-tangled, slant-sided farm; but Jeem, in his slow, soft-spoken way, said he couldn't think of any better place to live. A man could get perspective up there. So he bought back the mule his folks used to own, plowed up a corn patch, put in some potatoes, purchased a cow, and took up his whittling where he'd left off.

Though a man of few words, Jeem was a stanch credit to the countryside, and Mama and Grandma and the other happy housewives down in the valley set about finding a suitable wife for him. They paraded before him all their second, third, and fourth cousins' cousins, and nieces and friends' friends from the surrounding towns, for there were no more community girls left. It was the easiest thing in the world to arrange a meeting. All you had to do was to say, "Mary"—or "Clara" or "Jane," whatever the eligible girl's name happened to be—"I want you to go with me up to Jeem Hollister's and see his woodcarving," and Mary or Clara or Jane, being now in, or hovering near, the dreaded old-maid class, was always anxious to go, having been briefed on Jeem's six feet two and his wide, knotty shoulders, though they tried to feign non-interest by complaining of the long walk up the mountain. But they always went.

Sometimes if Mama or Grandma were too busy canning beans or cooking for harvesters, Mama had me and Molly Layton go along to show the way. Any girl who couldn't take over from there wouldn't be worthy of Jeem anyway. It was Molly and me who took Miss Kate, the new schoolteacher, up to Jeem's.

Miss Kate was pretty as a puccoon blossom with her yellow hair and brown eyes. If anybody could make Jeem forget Ginny Crawford it was the settled opinion of all that it would be Miss Kate. And she looked prettier than ever when he was showing her his carving. Of course, anybody would look pretty if they appreciated whittling when they saw Jeem's work. Even Molly's plain face was softened and it lighted up when she gazed at the intricate work which took up a good portion of his small living room.

Several years ago, before Jeem ever joined the army,

he had come upon an old knobby log that had once been a mighty tree brought to terms by a bolt of lightning which had left a jagged depression down the massive trunk. Later on, a windstorm had up-rooted its big, burry stump and for a year or more thereafter it lay in the forest, a perch for a squirrel or jay, and a favorite sunning place for green-tailed lizards. Lou and I hopped over the thing every morning and afternoon on our way to and from school. But it was Jeem, who spent lots of time in the woods, who discovered how much like the topographical contour of the valley the log was.

"See here," he said, his eyes alight with interest and none of his usual reticence in evidence, "this is the river down through the valley." He ran his finger along the depression made by the lightning. "Here are the mountains: Simms, Stono, Brown." He caressed the knobs and ridges. It was uncanny how much like the valley the log really was.

Jeem brought his mule down and snaked the log up to his house and no one heard any more about it until after he had gone to war and his mother, before she died, had asked some of the neighbors in to see her Jeem's whittlin'. Word got around about it and people made new paths up the mountain, going to see and to stand and study the masterpiece.

Jeem had removed the bark, sanded the log down to a smooth, satin finish, and set about making a wooden replica of the valley. And there it was to the tiniest detail, and all in perfect scale. Down at the far end of the valley, near the end of the log, was the river bridge spanning the lightning depression which was now our beloved river. It was made of the thinnest little pieces of hickory, and Jeem had even left a board loose in the bridge floor like it really was. Then there were the houses up and down the river—all exact models with the correct number of chimneys, windows, and doors. Ritter's. McFarland's. Britt's. Stacey's. Ours. And each one had its proper assortment of barns and outbuildings.

There was the stake-and-rider fence zigzagging up Simms Mountain, and the swinging bridge. Jeem had fixed it on tiny wire cables so it really would swing. Along the River Road was a horse and buggy, with Grandpa inside, driving. I think this tiny little spoke-wheeled buggy fascinated me more than anything. Then there were all the people, and you could have told who they were even if Jeem hadn't set them around their own homesteads, doing the things they did most. Lou and I in our sunbonnets he had put down in the pasture driving home some miniature cows. There was old Abe Adams with his slouch hat sitting on the steps of his summer kitchen. Mr. McFarland, wooden pitchfork in hand, was set in his barnyard, and Mrs. McFarland was hanging out wooden overalls.

No one was slighted. Even McDowells, with all their children, were all there. Some milking cows, some sawing wood, others in the garden. Jeem even threatened, with straight mouth but twinkling eye, to put in Slim Cole's still if he ever came across it, and folks said Slim traded off his best coon hound to Jeem to keep him from doing it.

At our place Jeem had put in the hounds, and, if

you can believe it, Tabby, the cat. She was no bigger
than your little fingernail, with a ridiculously tiny tail.

He had left his place until the last. Up on the
highest knob of the stump was the Hollister homestead, a slant-roofed cabin made of tiny logs with a
picket fence around it. Jeem had made his mother
and father and set them on a bench overlooking the
valley. Himself he had placed near the doorway and
he, of course, was whittling. The door to his home
was on tiny leathern hinges that allowed it to open
and shut. He was halfway through with the carving
of Ginny Crawford, who would, of course, have been
placed in the same dooryard, when he went away.
Folks said the first fire he built when he got back
home, he used the half carving of Ginny for kindling.

Everyone wanted Jeem to haul it all down to the
festival sometime, or put it on display over to the
city, but Jeem, never in a hurry, said it wasn't finished
yet; and by that we knew there was someone else to
go in Jeem's dooryard before he would call it com-
plete. And after Molly and I took Miss Kate up, Jeem
started whittling again and what we saw of it, it sure
looked like Miss Kate.

"Let's go up and see if it really is," I proposed to
Molly a while later, so after she'd tidied up the noon
dishes one day, we started. Molly took along a bucket
just in case we found any huckleberries.

We met Jeem coming down and he offered to go
back with us, but Molly wouldn't hear to it.

"We just wanted to see how you were coming along
on your piece," Molly said, blushing.

She always blushed when anyone looked straight at

her and Jeem always looked straight at anyone. His eyes not only looked—they appraised, too. Most times it was hard to tell what his appraisal was, but with Molly and me he always seemed more than satisfied. Of course I was just a kid.

"Well, go on up and in. The door's open," Jeem invited. "I'll be back after a while."

Molly said she didn't think we should, though, and we looked around for some huckleberries and luckily found a nice patch of ripe ones. We picked a gallon, all the time edging on up the mountain toward Jeem's place.

"Aw, come on, Molly, let's go on in," I begged when we got there. "Just to see if it is Miss Kate. Jeem won't care. He said so."

"Well, who cares if it is Miss Kate?" Molly said belligerently, sitting down on the step. "Go on in." It wasn't like her to be cross that way.

I never tired of looking at the carved valley and running my fingers over the hills and dales that my feet knew so well. Of course I looked at the Hollister place first to see if anyone new had been added.

"No one yet," I reported to Molly disappointedly, and then she came on in. Just like me, her eyes sought out the Hollister place first, but unlike me, that was all she was interested in and turned her attention elsewhere. She fluffed up a patchwork pillow in Jeem's chair, brushed some crumbs off the table, and swept wood shavings back into the fireplace. There were some cold, greasy fried potatoes sitting on the table and a flabby piece of side pork. Molly shuddered.

"Likely ain't had no proper cookin' for years," she

mumbled. Her eyes lit on our bucket of huckleberries and soon she was rummaging in Jeem's cabinet for flour and lard and sugar. Before he came back up the mountain she had a pie sitting under a cloth on the table, rich purple juices oozing out of the brown crusty slashes.

"Cook for everyone else 'round here. Don't see no reason why I can't cook for him," Molly mumbled, justifying herself, a smudge of flour graying her hair. I wished I could have been around when Jeem lifted that cloth for his supper, for Molly sure could cook.

I took up the next visitor all by myself. "Jeem, this is Grace Allen, Aunt Ellie's niece. She wants to see your carving," I said.

Jeem was chopping wood, but, of course, he quit and showed Grace his work. He never more than just pointed to it with his thumb, though. It was I who explained it all.

"My, my," Grace said, all big bug eyes and deep dimples, "I bet you cut your poor self a lot doing all this, don't you?" Her eyelids fluttered like a meadow lark settling on a millet stalk.

Grace's chances died a-borning.

"Here's something for you, kid," Jeem said as we were leaving. He handed me the prettiest little peach-seed ring you ever saw. "And take this to Molly."

It was a clumsily wrapped package. I could hardly wait to get back down the mountain to Molly to see what it was.

"For me?" Molly asked unbelievingly. No one ever gave her much except secondhand clothes.

"Sure, why not?"

Molly shrugged her shoulders deprecatingly and untied the package with excited hands. It was a carving of Jeem with his stomach rounded clear out of proportion, with one hand seeming to be patting it. There was an exaggerated Cheshire-cat look of satisfaction on his face like he was dying with pleasure. We laughed and laughed at the comical expression. It was his way of saying thanks for the pie. Jeem could talk better with his knife and a piece of hickory than anything else. Molly cleared everything off the shelf in her temporary room and put it in the exact center.

Before school started again I took up Alice Grant, Miriam Hastings, Sue Craft, and Maryanne Cleaver. "They want to see your carving, Jeem," I repeated each time. Jeem would have had to have been a Silly Willie indeed not to have caught on. They all "oo-ed" and "ah-ed" and then turned their eyelashy attention to Jeem. "Why don't you sell it, Mr. Hollister?" some asked. Others said, "My, don't you get awful lonesome way up here in this God-forsaken spot?" Others looked around the cabin, noting the dust on things and the wood shavings on the floor.

When I told Mama how the girls looked around at things, she sent Molly and me up to clean the place right away. "Why didn't I think about that before?" she demanded of herself.

"But he hasn't asked me to," Molly protested. "I can't just go barging in with a broom and mop when he hasn't asked me. I wouldn't know what to do."

"Oh, Molly. Just look around and do what you would do if you were living there. Make it pretty. Jeem always goes to town on Saturdays. Go up then and you won't bother him. I'll tell him I'm sending you."

Well, Molly really put her heart into it, once she got started. Most of Jeem's furniture he had made himself — a round pine table; ladder-back, hickory-bottom chairs; a fancy corner whatnot shelf. Molly polished and waxed until everything was softly gleaming. She knit a rag rug in the next few weeks and took it up, and made some blue-checked ruffled curtains for the windows. She cleaned and scoured the cooking pots and pans and fixed the furniture around a little more handily. If Jeem ever noticed any difference he never said so, which made Molly brave enough even to buy a blue bowl that matched the curtains to set in the center of the pine table.

"Gee, it sure is pretty, isn't it?" Molly would say, looking around proudly. "You think she'll like it?"

By "she" Molly meant Janice McFarland now, for the McFarlands had a niece who was out from town staying with them. They were asking Jeem down for a few Sunday dinners, and Jeem had taken Janice to a box supper. McFarlands had Molly come down to their house now and cook nice meals for Jeem when he came "a-callin' on Janice." It really looked like Molly was doing more to get Jeem a wife than anybody else.

When Molly would come back over to our house on special work days, Mama would ask her how things were between Janice and Jeem.

"Well, how should I know?" Molly stormed out, which again was unlike Molly.

"Well, you surely know how often he comes. And

how does he look at her? Can't you tell by the way
a man looks at a woman he loves her?" Mama demanded.

Molly blushed scarlet and said, "Nope," she reckoned she couldn't.

I knew Mama was sorry afterward she had asked
Molly such a question, she who, of all people, had
never had a beau in her life.

The next time Molly and I went up to clean Jeem's
house we could tell he was carving again, and it was
Janice all right. He had started with the head.

All the matchmakers sighed with relief and secretly started making quilts and pillowcases for Janice.
And Janice started making plans, too.

"First thing I'll do will be to get him down out of
that eagle's nest," she secretly confided to Mom.

After staying with various neighbors it was Molly's
turn to come back to our house. Sometimes Jeem
would bring his whittling down and set around the
fireplace with the rest of us and work on it. He was
taking more pains with the carving of Janice than
anybody, which was natural, of course. He'd hold it
up every once in a while and squint an eye at it to
get perspective. We'd all speak our admiration.

"What do you think of it, Molly?" he asked one
night, looking at her steadily like her opinion mattered.

"Me?" Molly looked up from her patching in surprise, blushing.

"Yes. You." Jeem spoke softly, but he was looking right into Molly's eyes, demanding an answer.

"Why, I—why, it's very pretty."

Jeem started whittling again. It seemed his concentration was out of proportion to his task, for he was almost through with it, just adding a few lines here and there. And then—snap, a little arm broke off. We all looked horrified. So much work all ruined. But Jeem was laughing.

"I knew it was across the grain from the beginning," he said, tossing the broken doll into the fireplace. We didn't know whether he meant the grain of the wood or his grain.

The matchmakers were disgusted. That was all, just plain disgusted. Jeem Hollister didn't want no woman, or if he did he'd just have to find one himself! They were through!

So I didn't get to go back up to Jeem's for a long time. There was no one else to take. It was winter anyway and hard to get up there. But the next spring, as soon as the dogwood started pokie-dotting the mountainside and the oaks put out little kitten-ear leaves, Jeem sent word around that his carving was finished and he'd be having an all-day party and singing come the second Saturday.

Jeem sent for Molly to come up and clean up things and get ready. I went along, too, but Mama said for me to hurry right back with the news of you-know-what if there was any. But since there wasn't any, I stayed around helping Molly clean and polish. Jeem had added the Ritters' new baby, and that was all.

Oh, he had torn off a little piece of Molly's blue-checked curtain not much bigger than a postage stamp and put it over the window on the inside of his little carved cabin home. I thought that was real nice since

Jeem never had said a thing about Molly's curtains she'd put up. But he had funny ways of doing things.

"There's a window on the other side, too," Jeem said, pointing to the little replica. "Maybe you'd better put a piece up at it, too, Molly. Just open the little door, and stick it up from the inside."

Molly took the scrap, opened the little door, and worked a long time, it seemed, getting the tiny piece put up.

"Can't you get it, Molly? Here, let me," I offered. My fingers were smaller.

"I got it," she said, choked-like, and then I noticed she was crying. Not out loud. Just standing there quietly letting the tears run down.

Jeem was standing across the room, watching her back. "Do you like it, Molly?" He spoke soft and low and stood so stiff and intense, as if it were the most important thing in the world to know how Molly liked it. "If you don't like it, Molly, I'll lock the little door and no one will ever know, but that's the way it will stay with me, always."

Such crazy talk. I didn't get it.

Finally Molly turned around and looked at him. She wasn't blushing this time and seemed like it made no difference at all to her that Jeem should see her crying. She smiled through her tears and said, "Yes, Jeem. I like it very much."

All the stiffness went out of Jeem and he sent me out to gather dogwood to pretty up the place. "Get a lot," he said.

Well, sometimes people were moved to tears by a

work of art and I guessed Molly appreciated good whittling as much or more than the rest of us.

The party was a big success in spite of the disappointed matchmakers. Everyone studied the wooden valley again and again in every detail. Seemed like it drew the people even closer together to see themselves all carved out of wood, each one going about his separate way of life, yet all being together like we were.

A crowd was all pushed around the log when I noticed the little blue-checked curtain in Jeem's carved house had come loose and I opened the miniature door to stick it back up like Molly had done. And then I saw it!

"Why, here's—" I began, and looked up quickly, searching for Molly's face. She winked and smiled. Then I looked at Jeem. He winked and smiled, too. I closed the little door softly, happy with my new secret. Why hadn't I guessed before? How long had it been that way?

"Jeem," someone was saying, "you haven't put Molly anywhere. Looks like she's been around here enough to be somewhere."

Then Jeem said in his soft, low-spoken way, "Molly's on there, all right. Right where she belongs." He nodded to me. "Open the little door, kid."

# Who Shall We Be Today?

LEFT TO our own impulses and ingenuity, Lou and I devised our own diversions. Some called it deviltry.

When the role of being the Bell young'uns began to pall, we were never ones to take it sitting down. For if we did there was no community organization to round us up, pamper our whimsies, and keep us out of trouble. And, if we evinced an over amount of apathy towards pulling weeds, hoeing corn, scrubbing, mopping, doing the dishes, and other chores, we were running the risk of being rejuvenated with one of Grandma's revitalizing teas.

So we dispelled any gloom brought on by the sameness of our days by the simple expedient of being different people ourselves. We might be Napoleon and Josephine, Sammy and Matt, Baucis and Philemon, or any number of characters with whom we were familiar.

"Who shall we be today?" Lou asked, as we crawled out of bed and pulled on our clothes.

"The Dutch Twins," I replied, ecstatically. Nothing, no life whatsoever appealed to me as much as the life of the Dutch Twins, portrayed in the series of twin books we had in our school library. To me their clean little home with tulips in the dooryard, as illustrated in the book, was the epitome of all that was good and clean and comfortable, and to desire any other mode of life was sheer nonsense.

"Aww, the Dutch Twins," Lou said, witheringly. "Let's be Damon and Pythias."

"Who were they?"

"Great friends."

"Well, gee, how can we play that—just great friends?" I asked, buttoning up my underwear.

"Pythias was going to die, see?" Lou squinted her eyes trying to remember so early in the morning.

"And what did she do? Damon?"

"She? They were boys!"

"Oh."

We worked in silence a while, trying to get our long underwear wound around smoothly. As winter waned the underwear legs stretched and stretched and by this time they would wind around two and a half times.

"I'm Pythias. I'm gonna die, see?" Lou explained.

"What from? Flu?"

"I've been condemned, see?"

"What's that?"

"They say I gotta die."

"Who?"

"Now, do you want to play this or not?" Lou's voice was getting impatient. "How do I know who says I gotta die."

I nodded that I did want to play, but I'd sure like

to know who it was that said someone else had to die. See?

"But I gotta leave town, and I say I'll be back at a certain time if they'll let me go, and you say if I'm not, you'll die for me, see?"

"Let me be Pythias."

"Naw, you're Damon. I can't make it back on time so you're all ready to die for me, see? Then I come running back in the nick of time to save you, and the lawyer, or whoever it was, forgives me and wants to be friends with us, too."

By this time we have finished dressing and start for the kitchen.

"But where do I wait on you if we're gonna play it?" I ask.

Lou stops halfway down the stairs, suddenly inspired.

"I've got to write a theme before we go to school this morning. I'll write it after breakfast, before I go help milk. You'll wait and wait and wait at the barn, willing to milk my cows if I don't show up. Then I'll come flying just in the nick of time!"

"You'll come flying," I repeated, to add emphasis to this portion of the plan.

"Whaddaya gotta die for?" I ask Lou, around the biscuit and sausage in my mouth.

Mama looks up, alarmed.

"Search me," Lou shrugs her shoulders.

"A game?" Mama inquires, hopefully.

We nod affirmatively, and everyone eats on in silence. After a while, Mama talks about her latest project. Over at the Rooks Hole on the river she plans to have Dad build some picnic tables and rustic chairs and she's going to put an ad in the *Farmington News* about it, hoping to rent it as a camp site. Lou and I think maybe we might be Thoreau-on-Walden there later.

At the barn I wait and wait and wait. Long since I have finished my cows, Anabelle, Trixy, and Trudy. Lou's cows wait patiently in their stalls for Pythias. My feet are cold and my hands freezing and I warm them in the fuzzy hair on the cows' udders. Ain't I supposed to die, and cheerfully, I remind myself? I am Damon, the faithful!

"Where's Lou?" Grandpa asks, coming by with the bucket of bran.

"She'll be here in the nick of time," I explain, cheerfully.

"Is Lou finished?" Dad asks, coming down his row of cows.

"I'm holding on for her," I explain.

"Holding on what?"

"Well, I mean she'll be here in the nick of time."

I strip Old Anabelle again, stalling, waiting. She looks around inquiringly. Polly, in the next stall, moos questioningly. "Where's Pythias?" she seems to say with her big brown eyes.

I listen for footsteps to come flying down the garden path. No Pythias.

"All finished?" Mom asks, starting toward the house with her two pails of milk.

"Not quite," I say, intimating only two more quarters to go.

"Well," I tell Damon. That's me. "If Pythias hadn't

come, wouldn't I have gone ahead?" So, taking fresh pails, I start in on Heart, Polly, and Primrose. Otherwise, the lawyer, Mom, will be waiting and wondering up at the separator. I am just half way through the last, Primrose, when Pythias comes rushing into the barn.

"Well, I made it," she exclaims, bright-eyed, and rosy-cheeked.

"I'm already three-fourths dead," I reply, accusingly. "I can no longer be Damon."

"Then we'll be someone else," she plans, taking my place on the stool and finishing Prim.

"The Dutch Twins," I say, ecstatically, willing to forgive.

"Oh, all right, the Dutch Twins," Lou agrees, after glancing at the withered bags of my own cows and hers, too.

Up in the attic in the trunk is a picture with the word "Degas" down in the corner. It is a picture of dancing girls in short, fluffy skirts. Only on a summer day when the pokeberries are ripe can we be Degas' dancing girls. With the ripe pokeberry juice we paint ballet slippers on our bare feet and lace them up, clear to our knees. Such a beautiful color, the magenta slippers! We shed our dresses, stuff our underskirts down in our drawers, and pin row on row of sycamore leaves around our middles, giving the effect of a short, ruffled skirt. Then away we go, whirling across the meadow, dipping and swaying, promenading, and do-si-doing, for we cannot stand on our toes like the girls in the picture.

Dad waves to us from the camp site where he is

just putting the finishing touches on the rustic chairs, and we wave back, wondering what queer peasant that could be, for we are Helene and Sylvia, skipping across the greensward of our stage, deftly avoiding the crawdad holes and other impedimenta of a cow pasture.

Sometimes we were Hans Brinker and skated all the way down the river to school. Gabriel and Evangeline we did with much aplomb, and once we even did Moses, climbing to the very tiptop of Stono Mountain and scratching some of the Ten Commandments on the limestone outcroppings there. Lots of times we were Christian in *Pilgrim's Progress,* especially when there were hard chores to do.

The very thought that we could be anyone we wanted to gave us a great sense of freedom. We were not just two little girls on a remote hill farm. We moved in and out of the pages of history and literature as blithely as a bluebird flew from one tree to another.

Once we got into roles that called for the addressing of one another as "thee" and "thou," and we went about for weeks with those words on our tongues.

"What's the matter with those kids?" we heard Dad ask Mom.

"Shhh, leave them alone. It's good for a person to believe he can be anyone he wants to."

But there was one role we had difficulty with. We discovered that the day the train jumped the track over by the Fifteen Acre Field. Lou and I were hoeing corn there. She was Alma Gluck and I Caruso and we were rendering "Sourwood Mountain." We stopped our hoeing to wave to the engineer and passengers as they went flying by. But right in front of our shocked and horrified eyes, the center car jumped the track and such a crash and bang and general hullabaloo you never saw. We rushed over to get a closer view before running home with the news, taking ringside seats on top of the right-of-way fence. People stood around in little groups talking excitedly. The conductors were passing through the crowd telling them that no one was injured and nothing was damaged but that it would be about an hour before help would come, so to make themselves comfortable in the shade.

A woman with a little boy spied us sitting on the fence and came over to ask if we knew how far they were from Fredericktown.

"Twenty mile," Lou said.

"You little girls live around here?" the lady asked.

"Yes," Lou replied.

The little boy, dressed in velvet pants and white ruffled shirt kept staring at us without blinking an eye. We thought him awfully rude.

"How far away is your home?" the lady asked.

"Mile," Lou replied, examining her tied-up toe.

"You scared or something?" the lady asked Lou.

"Nope."

The boy continued to stare. Finally he began tugging at his mother's sleeve and they turned and walked away.

"Are they hillbillies, Mother?" we heard Fauntleroy ask.

"Shh," she cautioned, looking back to see if we had

heard. "Yes, they're hillbillies, but don't let them hear you."

Lou and I turned questioning eyes upon each other. Then we rushed home to tell the news.

That night, as we were sitting on the porch watching the fireflies down in the meadow and listening to the whippoorwills along the creek, Lou asked, "Mom, what are hillbillies?"

"Well, they are just hill folks. They maybe live a little farther away from cities and towns than most folks. They mostly eat what they raise or find growing in the mountains. They live close to the earth and they don't like to owe money. They have a set of stories they pass on to their children, and a set of songs, too."

"Like what?"

"Oh, 'Barbara Allen,' 'Sourwood Mountain.' "

"We know those," I exclaimed.

"Why, of course," Mama says, then turning to Dad, she told him, "Wilson I had a letter from some folks interested in the camp site. They say they'll be along any day now."

The next morning when we got up, I asked, "Who we gonna be today?"

Lou thinks long and hard. "Let's be hillbillies."

So we try to be hillbillies. We don't know too much about these people, but we certainly have all the characteristics Mama described. We try and try to be hillbillies but we can find such little fun in it. What is there to do different from what we're doing? So we discard hillbillies and go on to the more glam-

orous Hansel and Gretel, Pocahontas and John Smith,
and Rumpelstiltskin.

"Isn't it good to be able to be anyone you want to?"
Lou asks.

"Yeah," I say, only faintly worried about the difficult role of the hillbillies.

"Do you want to try hillbillies again?" I ask the
next day while we're sitting beside the road waiting
for the mail carrier.

"Naw."

"Why not?"

"Aww, it's too easy. It's just like pretending to be
a frog when you are a frog."

"Then we are hillbillies?" I ask.

She shakes her head affirmatively.

"Well, good. I was beginning to doubt that we
could be anyone we wanted to."

"Let's be Ananias the Liar." she proposes. We'd
just studied about him in Sunday School.

"Oh, I don't think we ought to," I said, alarmed.

"It's all right, just as long as we're pretendin'."

"Yeah, but maybe people won't know we're pretendin'."

"We can tell 'em later."

I sit pondering about this while a car comes lumbering down the rough, rocky road. To our surprise, it
stops in front of us.

"How far is it to the St. Francis River?" the driver
asks.

" 'Bout fifty miles," Lou says, and I clap my hand
to my mouth in shock. We are exactly a half mile
from the river now.

"You sure?"

"Yep," Lou vouches.

"Ever hear of a place called the Rooks Hole?" the man inquires.

"Never heard of it," Lou declares.

"Well, I'm a son-of-a-gun, I've been looking all over for it," the man says and lumbers on down the road that takes him back to town.

"How you going to tell him you were just pretendin'?" I ask Ananias.

Lou looks only faintly worried. The mail comes and we hurry back home. We are the Pony Express and Apaches are on our trail. Ananias has played his brief role.

"Will thee pass me the tomatoes?" Lou asks me at the supper table.

"Thou hast had more than I and there are only two slices left," I reply.

"Thee take one and I will take one," Lou offers.

"Thou first." I pass her the platter.

"I just can't understand it," Mom says.

"I can't either. Can't you kids talk like the rest of us?" Dad asks.

"No, I mean about the campers," Mom says. "They should have been here by now. You reckon they got lost?"

Ananias paused with a slice of tomato in mid-air. She turns slow eyes toward mine. "I tell you what," she says, appeasingly, "Let's play the Dutch Twins."

# The Treasured Wealth

JEANIE," Mom asked, turning from the telephone, "have we got the "P" book?"

"I don't know," I said, glancing at the bookcase.

"No, Clem McDowell has it," Lou volunteered. "He just got through giving a report on pigmies at school."

"Lonnie?" Mom turned back to the telephone. "Lou says McDowells have it. Their phone's out of order, though. I'll have the kids stop by when they go after the mail and pick it up for you."

It was the telephone being out of order that accounted for any of us having the "P" book or the "A" book or any other of the twenty-six-volume community-owned set of encyclopedia.

What books we owned before we acquired a one-thirteenth interest in this set, we knew by heart. There was the black-bound, black-flyleaved *Pilgrim's Progress* Grandma had brought through the Cumberland Gap, an awesomely illustrated book for young eyes, but not so fearfully impressive as the still blacker bound *Night Scenes from the Bible.* In its many illustrations the skies were always stormy and the inevitable waves mountain high. Moses, clasping a stone tablet to his chest, fearsome eyes turned toward a lightning-split sky, made Lou and me shiver involuntarily and push the book back in a far corner of the bookcase, behind Douglass's fat *History of Southeast Missouri*.

There were two green-bound volumes of Scott's "Waverley Novels" with gold thistles on the front. Where they came from no one could remember. We had a flower-covered, gilt-edged volume of *Byron's Poems; Romola; Riders of the Purple Sage; Billy Sunday's Sermons; The Shepherd of the Hills; Eight Cousins;* a softly padded leather-bound volume of *Longfellow's Poems; The San Francisco Earthquake,* and *The Great Chicago Theater Disaster.* These latter two were studied in much detail, there being pictures of most of the deceased, and we liked pictures. We could give the names and addresses of three fourths of them as easily as we could say our nines in multiplication.

"It's not enough for the children," Mama often lamented when she had heard us, for about the third or fourth time, read *Riders of the Purple Sage,* or *Evangeline* aloud to Grandma. Grandma never complained, though, and had great patience when we tried to wade through the "Waverley Novels." Come to a sad part, the tears would stream down her face as freely as they did ours, and sometimes she'd make us back up and read again something funny, though she'd heard it thirty times before.

When the day came that I could sit down and "read" whole chapters from *Eight Cousins* without the book, Mama even cried.

"It's a shame," she complained to Dad and Grandma and Grandpa, and even to us kids. "It isn't as if they didn't like to read or couldn't. It's such a waste." She shook her head forlornly.

But, money being so hard come by, it was out of the question to buy any more books.

The winter the schoolteacher stayed with us she brought out her books and we were introduced to Thoreau and Hawthorne.

"Go back and read that again," Mama demanded, when we came to the part in *Walden* that said, "Books are the treasured wealth of the world, and the fit inheritance of generations and nations. Books, the oldest and best, stand naturally and rightfully on the shelves of every cottage. They have no cause of their own to plead, but while they enlighten and sustain the reader his common sense will not refuse them."

*"Common sense will not refuse them,"* Mama repeated under her breath, looking grim.

Book salesmen did not venture into the rural territory then, and especially not to such places as ours. Standard directions out from town were: "After you cross the M.R. & B.T. railroad tracks, go a piece 'til you come to a big blazed sycamore. A hundred or so rods farther on, turn to the right and go 'til you strike a creek. It might be dry in summer. Take the south fork 'til you come to the old Bonahan farm, then head up the hill to the Big Field, follow the rail fence down to the river and a spell on the other side is a lane leading up to the Bells." What salesman would have tried it? And what salesman in his right mind would expect to sell a set of fifty-dollar encyclopedia to farmers who could barely rake up the money for the interest?

No salesman would have, either, unless aided and abetted by Mama.

There were few coincidences in our lives comparable to the one that took Mama and a book salesman on the same Saturday morning to Aunt Grace's house in the nearest town.

Mama and Lou and I went in Aunt Grace's kitchen door with our weekly supply of butter and eggs for her. We heard her in the parlor talking and waited for her to come out.

"Myrtle, that you?" she inquired, coming into the kitchen. "Wait'll I get rid of this salesman," she whispered, making a wry face.

"What kind?" Mom asked.

"Books." Aunt Grace looked properly put out.

"Could we see them?" Mama asked, tentatively, brushing the bangs back out of my eyes and smoothing the wrinkles from Lou's dress.

"Why, sure. What for?"

"Oh, the kids like books."

"Well, don't encourage him or he'll never go," Aunt Grace said, leading the way back.

Red leather bound they were, with gold lettering, and an imprint of the globe on the front. We ran our fingers in the depressions made by the longitudes and latitudes. Big, fat, thick books with lots of pictures. There on the first page was an aardvark, and we didn't even know there was such an animal!

Mama picked up the "B" book. "Here's Babylon," she said, reverently. We looked on with interest. The only picture of Babylon we had seen was in *Night Scenes,* and it was scary.

"See. Here's the Hanging Gardens," Mama pointed out.

"They belonged to Nebuchadnezzar II," Lou added. We knew that from *Night Scenes.* I think it was Lou's knowing that that turned the salesman's attention from Aunt Grace to us. And, after all, Mom did have on her salmon-colored Indianhead linen. Lou had her watch on and we were wearing our patent-leather slippers, not too run-down.

"You like books?" the salesman inquired, hitching his chair closer, interested.

"They are the treasured wealth of the world," Mama murmured, turning to "Bach, Johann Sebastian."

The salesman adjusted his bifocals, and cleared his throat. One little stray hair in his moustache quivered.

"Do you have many?"

"Only a few," Mama replied, sadly.

"Well, now. . . ." The salesman abandoned Aunt Grace completely. "Frankly I don't see how any mother expects to raise children in this enlightened day and age without having a set of these in her home."

"Neither do I," Mama said, devoutly. "They stand naturally and rightfully on the shelves of every cottage."

"Right you are," the salesman exclaimed delightedly. "Let me say it is a rare pleasure to meet someone who holds books in their proper esteem. If you do not already own a set, naturally you want one."

"Naturally," Mama replied, picking up another book and thumbing through it.

"Myrtle!" Aunt Grace demanded. "Do you know how much they cost?"

"Humm?" Mama asked, looking up.

"They're fifty dollars!" Aunt Grace warned with flashing eyes.

"Well worth it," Mama said, closing the book and running her hand appraisingly over the grainy cover.

The salesman's head was busy flying back and forth from Aunt Grace to Mom while he listened to Mom sell his books. He smiled smugly and got out his order blank. The moustache hair quivered vigorously.

"How did you wish to pay for them, Mrs. Bell?"

"What?" Mama looked at him quickly.

"Well, you can save some by paying cash," he said, his face a little flushed and his fingers nervous with his sale.

"Oh, but I couldn't buy them," Mama said, looking up, alarmed.

"But I thought you said. . . ."

"Oh, no. No, I didn't say anything like that," Mama replied, wide-eyed, laying the book down hastily.

The salesman buttoned up his vest, adjusted his bifocals again, wiped his forehead, tweaked his moustache, losing the hair, and started in all over again.

"Young lady," he said, turning to me. "Tell me, do you know what a duck-billed platypus is?" His eyes bored into mine, accusingly. I stepped back, embarrassed, and acknowledged, shame-faced, that I didn't.

"And you," he went on, looking at Lou, "do you know where the House of Seven Gables is?"

"Salem, Massachusetts," Lou replied, calmly. "And the Old Manse is at Concord," she added for good measure.

Mama smiled indulgently at Lou. "They know Hawthorne," she explained, trying to hide her pride.

"Mrs. Bell," the salesman said, changing his tactics in midstream, "allow me to say you have two very precocious youngsters here." He was being generous with me.

I didn't know what "precocious" meant, but it sounded good and I was glad to be included, in spite of the "padded puss" or whatever it was.

"Sometimes in our rush of living, we overlook the most important things," he went on sadly. "Think what a set of these books would mean to these wonderful little girls." His voice turned low and confidential. "You know, I have a couple of youngsters, too, and we lived on practically bread and water 'til I got a set of these books in the hands of my children." He wiped his eyes and sighed. I felt my own eyes stinging.

"How much did you say they were?" Mom asked, hesitantly, after a moment of silence while we sat thinking about the bread and water.

The salesman whipped out his order pad again.

"Only fifty dollars, Mrs. Bell," he pleaded. "Think of it! The world at your fingertips. You can pay just five dollars down and the rest in monthly installments."

"But we don't want none, Mister," Aunt Grace put

in, severely. "And if you don't mind, I've some things to do."

The salesman looked at Mama and Mama looked at Lou and me a long time. She brushed the bangs back again, straightened Lou's belt. Finally, she said, "I'll take them," in a clear, determined voice. We bit our lower lips incredulously.

The salesman looked at Aunt Grace haughtily, pocketed his handkerchief, and sat down. In less than five minutes he was gone with Mama's five-dollar bill that she was going to get coffee and sugar and flour and corn meal with.

"Well, Myrtle, what will the rest of them say?" Aunt Grace demanded.

Lou and I turned questioning eyes to Mama, too. Yeah, what would they say?

"Well, I don't care what they say." Mama's voice was only a little shrill as she kept snapping and unsnapping her pocketbook, peering down into the little dark recess where the five-dollar bill had been. But forty-five minutes later, when we'd passed the old Bonahan place, coffeeless and flourless, it was a whole lot shriller and quivery on top of that. And by the time we'd gotten to the Big Field, we were all quietly crying, though we hadn't talked about the books at all.

"I'll stop here at Britts," Mama said, pulling in old Maude and the buggy to the hitching post, "and phone back to Aunt Grace to stop that salesman."

We were glad there was a way out, though we were sorry to see the lovely books go so quickly. Where did an aardvark live, anyway?

"Lonnie," Mama explained to Mrs. Britt, "I've done an awful thing and I want to use your phone."

"It's out of order, Myrtle."

"Out of order!" Mama wailed—as if they weren't almost half the time.

"What is it, Myrtle? What have you done?" Lonnie asked, alarmed, looking around at our tear-stained faces.

Mom explained while Mrs. Britt shook her head commiseratingly.

"I know just how it is, Myrtle," she sympathized. "Once I let a salesman talk me into buying a carpet sweeper and you know I haven't had a carpet in my whole life. She laughed ruefully.

"Oh, it isn't as if I don't want the books, Lonnie," Mom said. "It's just that I should have known we couldn't pay for them. I'll just have to drive back and get my five dollars back and cancel the order."

So we flew back to town as fast as old Maude could go. But we were too late. The man had already left town on the noon train.

"You wouldn't have gotten your money back anyway, Myrtle," Aunt Grace said, accusingly. "Didn't you read the contract? It said if for any reason it was canceled, the down payment remained the property of the company."

Even old Maude's ears drooped on our way back home and her rump swayed dejectedly.

Lonnie Britt was waiting out by her gate to see how things came out.

"We were too late," Mom reported.

"Aw, now, ain't that too bad," Mrs. Britt said,

wrapping her arms in her big white apron and clucking her tongue. It was good to have Lonnie Britt on your side in time of trouble.

"Well, now don't you worry none, Myrtle. Ain't no sense in worrying over that. Now, if it was cholera in the hogs or the river floodin' out the crops, it would be different. But, pshaw, this ain't nothin'!"

Dad and Grandma and Grandpa never said one word when Mama confessed at the supper table. That was the awful part of it. Dad just kept evening up his knife and fork with the edge of the table, starting to say something and then not saying it. Grandma passed the spoon holder around three times and Grandpa started to put his usual two spoonfuls of sugar in his coffee, but thinking better of it he dumped the second one back in the bowl.

"I'll just write them a letter and tell them not to send the books," Mama concluded after days of worry.

"Oh, let 'em come," Grandma said. "At least we can look at them and then send them back."

"Yeah," Lou and I pleaded. "How long was that aardvark's nose anyway?"

I wondered if this wouldn't be a good time to cash in some of the A.T. & T.

The books were so long in coming we were half hopeful they wouldn't. By the time they did arrive, which was the very day when the neighbors were over helping with the threshing, news had spread through the community of Mama's great indiscretion.

"Gonna educate 'em all up, are you, Miz Bell?" Tom Alexander joked. And Jim Stacey said, "Now if

I'd knowed you was hankering for books, we wouldn't have used up that old Sears catalog."

Mama couldn't come back at them for, of course, she didn't actually know how she was going to pay for the books.

"Don't you pay them no mind now, Myrtle," Lonnie Britt said, cutting huge squares of corn bread. She'd come over to help with the cooking. "Do you all good if you did a little more book reading," she railed out at the menfolk. "And you, Tom, how about that time you bought the fiddle without no strings nor a bow? You, Jim, you still got that stereoscope that salesman sold you without any pictures for it?"

Jim and Tom looked a bit sheepish, shuffled their feet under the table, and asked for more potatoes and beans.

"Now I tell you what we're going to do," Lonnie said, decisively. "We're all going to buy those books. And we're all going to use 'em. Now, Tom, you fork over a couple of dollars and take the 'A' book. Let Bells keep the 'B' book. Crawfords will take the 'C' book. Keeping 'em alphabetical, we'll know where they are most of the time." Lonnie warmed to her plan. "And where there's two 'B's' like me and Bells, we'll have one take a letter that isn't in the community, like 'G.' You keep the 'G' book anyway, Myrtle. You've already got five dollars in it and are entitled to two books."

Well, that's the way it was in spite of Mama's protestations. Like I said, it was good to have Lonnie on your side in time of trouble.

We did the "A" book from Aachen, a city in western Germany, to Azurite, a colored mineral, then took it back to Alexanders. We studied our own "B" book from Alexander Graham Bell, some of our kinfolks, we hoped, to the Byzantine Empire.

It wasn't altogether satisfactory, though, because just as sure as you wanted one particular book to look up something in, it was five miles down the river, and when you got down there it had been loaned to someone five miles back up the river. And sometimes people wouldn't let you keep a book until it was thoroughly digested—a thing we liked to do, but we didn't feel in a position to argue about it, for the whole system was set up more or less for our benefit. Then, too, folks got the idea that Lou and I were just the proper legs for this circulating library. Down to Ritters with this book. Up to McFarlands with that. Over to Staceys with another.

"We can't complain," Mom said, "but I wish we could have kept them all."

That first year, in addition to our own "B" and "G" books, we got as far down as the "H" book. But it was the "B" and "G" we knew by heart.

Someone suggested once that the books be gathered up and taken over to the school, but there were too many against that for everyone was proud to have an encyclopedia on the parlor table by the Bible. So proud, in fact, that they quit teasing Mom. There was some new joke by this time anyway. It had to do with Archie McDowell's buying one of the new electric radios with electricity still five miles down the river, too.

This was what they were all laughing about when

we were at the Fourth-of-July picnic the next summer when I tried to get them all quiet.

It wasn't long after we'd spread our picnic lunch
when I came running up with my news. Lonnie Britt
was folding up the tablecloths. Elsie Crawford was
feeding her baby. Mom was putting away remnants
of a cake. Some of the menfolks were clearing a place
for horseshoes and laughing at Archie and his radio.

"Come on. Come on," I yelled to them all, trying
to make them hear me.

"What is it, Jeanie?" Mama looked alarmed, hastily
untying her apron.

"Just come on. Everybody." I turned and ran and
motioned for them to follow, looking back over my
shoulder to see that they did. And they did. Just
like I was the gingerbread man, and them all strung
out behind me. I got so far ahead I had to stop at
the merry-go-round to make sure they saw which way
I turned, and again at the Ferris wheel. But they kept
coming, Mama's hair falling loose, Grandma clutch-
ing her old pocketbook, Tom Alexander picking up
one of the little ones and carrying him along, Elsie
Crawford with her baby crying, Archie McDowell
holding onto a broken suspender, Cabe Ashton with
a horseshoe in his hand.

Right up onto the wooden platform I ran while
they all came up running and stopped short and
breathless down below.

The announcer was saying, "Here's the little lass
who wants to try it. Remember, folks. If she can get
all the way through without a mistake, we will give

a dollar for every word. There's been fifteen try it already but so far no one has made it. Are you ready?"

I nodded that I was. How many words did the thing have, anyway? What would I get with all that money? I'd buy all the books back anyway. Bless the dear "G" book. Or get another set. I looked at Lonnie Britt standing down below, looking up at me so proudly. I'd get Lonnie a carpet to go with her carpet sweeper if it was only a couple of throw rugs. That was for sure. I almost stumbled and missed a word when I thought about the strings and bow for Tom's fiddle and pictures for Jim's stereoscope. Maybe I could even get electricity brought up to the community for Archie's radio. That was it! I'd bring electricity up the valley for it was too dark to read in the old kitchen, and there was a hole already bored over the table for the fixture. Did electric bills run big, I wondered, but kept on.

How triumphant Mama looked. I saw her lips moving and it looked as if she was saying, "They are the treasured wealth of the world." Lou was repeating the thing silently with me. Dad was counting on his fingers, but he finally had to give that up. A hush had fallen over the whole crowd. Even the Ferris wheel and merry-go-round had stopped. Elsie Crawford's baby wasn't making a sound. A locust in the tree above me shrilled down to a dead stop and I wound up magnificently, ". . . that this nation, under God, shall have a new birth of freedom; and that government of the people, by the people, for the people shall not perish from the earth."

# *Auction Sale!*

BRITTS' bull was a brindled, curly, thick-necked
tormentor, who roamed the pasture on the neigh-
boring farm, bellowing profanely, hoisting his pedigreed tail arrogantly, and pawing the ground vicious-
ly when anyone came within range of his dark, evil,
thick-lashed eyes. And twice a day on our way to and
from school, Lou and I came within range of those
ever-watchful, all-seeing eyes. Even when we took off
our red sweaters and stuffed them under our dresses
and tiptoed along the path that ran beside the pasture, he'd see us. Clear across the field he'd come,
his stub-ugly old horns growing longer and longer with
every inch of ground he covered, and we'd cling in
trembling desperation to one another, knowing that
this time the fence couldn't hold such fury.

About three weeks straight of this bovine torture
was all we could take and we'd resume our secret de-
tour to school—across Simms Mountain and down the
Cedar Bluffs, scuffing our shoes on the boulders and
tearing our dresses and stockings on the sawbriers and
being inevitably a half hour tardy both ways. Then
Mom would catch on and she'd go with us several
mornings again to show us there was nothing to be

afraid of. She'd throw sticks and rocks at the bull to get him really infuriated, and we'd grudgingly admit that the fence truly was bull-proof and stuff our fear down into some subconscious region.

But the dreams were worse than the reality. Each night the bull skimmed over the fence as if it were only a cobweb and chased us, his breath hot on our heels, to some never-reached, ever-elusive point of safety for half the night, or until we fell out of bed. Then we'd have to go through the wearisome, wakening process of groveling our way out of the paralyzing remnants of panic, with only the dismal thought that tomorrow we'd have to pass the fearsome old monster again.

No wonder we were beside ourselves with joy when we saw the notice on the telephone pole that Britts were having a sale. We read every word:

### AUCTION SALE

One coal-and-wood range, kitchen table and chairs, brass bedstead, 8-day clock, 5 gal. cedar churn, gramaphone records, straw ticks, and other household items too numerous to mention. Plows, harrows, cultivators. Singletrees, horse collars, corn grinders. Chickens, calves, pigs, and

### A REGISTERED JERSEY BULL.

This latter, neatly centered in capital letters, lent prestige to all that went before and would be a powerful drawing card. We talked about it effusively, our words tumbling out with the ragged enunciation of the emotionally relieved. Of course we hated to see our good friends move. But they were just going into town and we could see them on Saturdays, while there were possibilities that the bull would be taken clear out of the country. Maybe as far as St. Louis anyway, or even to Chicago! We happily envisioned his hideless rump hanging in the rooms at National Stockyards.

Lou and I went through our possessions carefully to see what we might have to sell. It was anyone's privilege to bring whatever he had to a neighborhood sale and enjoy the service of the hired auctioneer. It made for bigger crowds, stiffer bidding, and higher morale.

We wanted some cash money to send off for the perfume advertised on the back of the magazine that would "open the secrets of love" for us. Though our physical growth had been stunted by the bull we were emotionally normal. We decided to part with the doll bed and cradle that we had long ago put aside. Mom was taking the old incubator, and Grandma had an extra rag rug she had knit during the winter.

Valley folks usually took a basket dinner, or if a big crowd was expected out from town, the Ladies Aid served lunch. A big crowd was expected at Britts on account of the registered bull.

On the morning of the sale, Lou and I were on our way as soon as the sun peeped over Gillman's Hill. Mom and Grandma were coming later, after they had fixed their quota of sandwiches.

McDowells, Ritters, Claytons and Staceys, all in spring wagons piled high with "auction loot," passed us on the way, offering to let us ride, but we preferred to walk. The day was mild and good-smelling.

There would be others walking whom we might join along the way, and the pleasure of the day would be enhanced by prolonged anticipation.

We saw old Granny Weaver coming down Gold Mine Hollow and waited for her to catch up with us. She had one of her quilts carefully wrapped in newspapers.

"Which one you taking, Granny?" Lou asked. Granny's quilts were known far and wide and were the needlework pride of the valley, next to Grandma's Passage-of-Time quilts.

"The Sunset on Stono," she replied firmly, as if the decision had been long and arduous.

"Oh, Granny! That's your prettiest one," I objected. We knew the quilt well, as did everyone for miles around. It was an original Granny had designed. There were the pine trees done in shaded greens, looking for sure like they did when the sun was low in the west. She had others she was saving against taxes and groceries—the Wedding Ring, Drunkard's Path, Flower Garden, Doves in the Window—but none as pretty as the Sunset on Stono.

"Well, I thought it would bring me more money than the others, and I'm after that brass bedstead. Did you know it used to belong to me?"

We shook our heads negatively.

"Simm told me before he died never to let go of it. Said I'd always see my way clear if I kept the brass bedstead. He was funny about things like that toward the last. Out of his head most of the time." Granny was talking more to herself now than to us, but we walked along quietly, respecting the dignity of her age and listening to her tell about old Grandpa Weaver, who was dead long before we came to the valley.

Granny stopped to rest often. She was old—near eighty. Where the path came out on a clearing she shifted her quilt to the other side and stood looking out over the valley a long time, as though she were catching up on her memories.

"Always wish I'd kept the bedstead," she went on. "I recollect the day Simm hauled it up the mountain in the oxcart. We had a fresh straw tick waiting and two feather beds, one out of wild goose feathers and one out of tame. I spread my Rose of Sharon quilt on it, and a handsomer sight you never saw, the round knobs catching the sunlight and making a white rainbow on the ceiling. All our babies were born in that bed, and Simm died in it. He'd raise up in the dead of the night, get holt of a knob and say, 'Always keep this, Dulcie. Always keep this.' But then times were hard after Simm died and when Lonnie Britt offered me good money for it. I had to let it go. You can't let sentiment get the best of you when you're hungry. But if I had it to do over I'd have gotten a little hungrier."

"Maybe she'd sell it back to you, Granny, instead of putting it up for bid," Lou suggested.

"No, I won't be asking no favors. 'T ain't our way. Might be someone out from town can pay her more, but I'm counting on my quilt bringing enough to bid up on it. I'll have to sell it first, though," Granny said, unabashed. We were all confounded about cash.

We walked along in silence for a while, thinking about the brass bedstead.

"Reckon hit'll bring the price of the bed?" Granny asked after a while.

"Why, sure, Granny," Lou reassured her. Wait'll those ladies out from town see it. And I don't imagine there'll be much bidding on the bedstead."

"I reckon I've never wanted anything as bad in my whole life as I want that brass bedstead back," Granny confessed, a little embarrassed, as if she should be ashamed of such desires. She looked at us a little defiantly, daring us to challenge her right to want the brass bedstead so badly, but Granny couldn't have found a more understanding audience. We'd felt that way so many times. There were the ribbon-threaded celluloid fans and glass beads at Wallingford's Mercantile, fountain pens and vanity cases, and now the perfume. And to think that Granny, who was so much older than we were, had been wanting her bedstead back for so long!

We heard the auctioneer singsonging his bids a long way off and hurried on so as to miss as little as possible. He was doing the harness and machinery first, to give the town folks time to arrive.

Lou and I put our name on the doll bed and cradle and set them down in the yard with the other household goods. There were quilts and coverlets and a peacock-embroidered bedspread hung for display over the clothesline, and Granny unwrapped her quilt and hung it up, too.

Folks started arriving from town about ten o'clock

and began plundering through the things set out in the yard.

"Jane, come here and see this clock!" some woman demanded.

"I wish you'd look at that hand-woven coverlet," another woman said, sucking in her breath. When they saw Granny's quilt, oh's and ah's went up in unison.

"Oh, I must have that," someone said. And, "Not if I can help it," another answered.

The crowd of women stood around the quilt for half an hour or longer, admiring the beautifully shaded colors, the tiny stitches, and the intricate quilting design. Granny stood off to one side, smiling contentedly. Soon she was pointed out as the owner of the quilt, and various women began approaching her ever so casually, making whispered offers for the quilt. Mrs. Whittaker started with ten dollars, but Granny shook her head. The doctor's wife offered fifteen, and Granny wavered. When Mrs. Catherton offered twenty, Granny took it. "After all, they might not sell the quilts first, and I've got to have the money before I can bid on anything else," she reasoned.

The brass bedstead, propped up against a maple, aroused little interest. "Look at that old relic," someone jeered. "All those curlicues to dust, I wouldn't have it on a bet." We jubilantly relayed the news to Granny.

About noon the men drifted up to the yard. Cabe was with them. It was on account of him that I wanted the perfume. I could see his eyes searching the crowd. When he saw me he jerked his head back-

ward in an awkward, impersonal acknowledgment, but
his eyes stopped wandering about and I put all my
confused attention on the auctioneer who was starting in on the small stuff. Our bed and cradle came
before long, and we got a dollar for them. Lou was
tempted to bid with it on a beaded and fringed pocketbook made from an old red inner tube, but I held
out for the perfume, and she agreed that it would be
better if it just weren't for the interminable waiting
for it to arrive once it was ordered.

While the auctioneer went through the books and
pots and pans and canned goods, Lou and Granny
and I leaned up against the old brass bedstead to
hide it from interested eyes. But it didn't work.

"Let's see this," some strange girl said, indicating
that she wanted us to move so she could look at the
bedstead.

"This old thing?" Lou scoffed, looking shocked.

"Mother, come here," the girl said, ignoring Lou's
remark. "Look! This is just like what I saw in the
magazine. It was painted pink and had a white bedspread. Oh, Mama! Wouldn't it be pretty?"

The woman reached out a hand to test the weight
of the headpiece. Her diamonds sparkled in the sunlight, and Lou and I looked at each other in dismay.
"You sure this is what you want, Lovey?" the woman
asked.

"Oh, yes, Mama! And we'll get the white rug, like
it was in the picture."

*White rug!* I watched Lou's Adam's apple do a
quick up and down. We both looked guardedly at
Granny, who was just standing there looking at the

woman, nervously clasping and unclasping the noisy latch on her old pocketbook.

The woman beckoned to the auctioneer, and he immediately came over and started auctioning the bedstead.

"One dollar!" Granny opened.

"Five dollars," the woman said, calmly, and folks did a double take at the old bedstead.

"Five dollars, ten cents," Granny kept on.

"Ten dollars."

"Ten dollars, ten cents."

"Fifteen."

The interested crowd pushed closer, wondering what in the world anyone wanted with the old bed.

"She'll never stop," Lou whispered, disgusted by such wealth, and we noticed the tears brimming in Granny's eyes.

"Fifteen dollars, ten cents," she said in an unsteady voice, knowing it was her last bid if the woman kept jumping five. I felt the tears stinging at my eyes.

The auctioneer was happy at the turn of events and took a few minutes off to joke with the crowd. I turned around and saw Cabe right behind me.

"What's the matter?" he whispered, bending down.

"Granny wants it so badly," I said unsteadily, "and she's only got twenty dollars." Cabe turned his pockets wrong side out, indicating he was in the same shape as the rest of us.

In the meantime the bidding had resumed.

"Twenty!" the woman said, looking unruffled but resigned, as if she was prepared to go on to a hundred or more.

Granny made her way to the back of the crowd, her narrow little shoulders looking more humped than ever.

"Twenty, once," the auctioneer warned. "Twenty, twice!"

Cabe suddenly pushed his way up through the crowd. The auctioneer thought he was a new bidder and gave him a little time to inspect the bed. Cabe unscrewed one of the lopsided, loose-fitting brass knobs, looked into it, gave a low whistle, shrugged his shoulders, hastily put the knob back on and walked off, wiping his hands on his overalls.

A knowing titter passed through the crowd. Slow grins spread over faces.

"Bugs," someone surmised audibly.

"Twenty, three times and —" the auctioneer appeared in a hurry to be done with it now.

"Twenty-one!" Lou shouted.

The auctioneer turned to the strange woman, motioning that it was her time to bid, but she, too, was disappearing toward the back of the crowd, shuddering.

"Twenty-one, once," the auctioneer now continued. "Twenty-one, twice, three times, and sold to the little girl in the blue dress."

Lou walked up proudly to claim her prize. If bedbugs were the only thing in the world she had to cope with, her troubles were over.

"Run and get Granny," she whispered to me, pulling the dollar out of her pocket and handing it to the cashier with a staunch vow that the rest of it would be there soon.

I searched the crowd frantically for Granny.

"Yonder she goes," someone said, pointing down the road where Granny was just disappearing around the first bend.

"I'll go get her," Cabe offered, and started out at a run.

Granny was beaming with joy when she came puffing back up the road. She finished the payment and carried the bedstead back and leaned it up against the tree caressingly.

"Bless you, child," she kept mumbling, stroking Lou on the head.

"Don't bless me," Lou said. "Bless him." She pointed to Cabe. Granny didn't know what it was all about, but kept reassuring Lou she'd pay her the dollar soon as she got one.

"Oh, that's all right," Lou said, as if the perfume was the last thing in the world she wanted now.

I looked at Cabe, his hair blue-black in the bright sun and his big strong hands helping the auctioneer move a dresser. More than ever I wanted the magic perfume!

The rest of the day passed pleasantly. Mom and Grandma brought extra sandwiches for us and we had a glass of lemonade for lunch. In the afternoon, sitting in the shade of the grape arbor, Lou and Maryellen, with much giggling, planned the parties and dates they would have when Lou would come to town to stay all night with Maryellen. When the shadows began to lengthen, families started to load up and go home. Where a rug or rocking chair had been hauled to the sale, a perforated tin cupboard or ten-gallon crock might be making the return trip. We saw Jeptha

Alexander put a coop full of squawking pullets in the back of his spring wagon, and someone out from town tied a cow to the back of his buggy. Everything going off in different directions, I thought sadly, and was gladder than ever that at least the bedstead was going back to an even earlier home.

"Who bought the bull?" Lou suddenly demanded, for in the excitement of the day we had forgotten this thing of all things. And then, because Maryellen was there, and because we had never let her know how we felt about their bull, we passed it off as a joke and acted uninterested.

Cabe was going to haul Granny and her bedstead home and he asked Lou and me if we wanted to ride, too.

From the wagon bed we saw the auctioneer still busy selling the remnants of the farm tools. The bull, pawing and snorting, was tied securely in his pen until his new owner came to cart him away. We waved good-by to him in mock sorrow, singing jubilantly, "I'll be glad when you're dead, you rascal you."

Cabe said he wished he could have bought him. "Wouldn't take long to build up a good herd. A man could get ahead with pedigreed stock."

The wagon road didn't go all the way to Granny's cabin. It was too steep and rocky, so we climbed out and carried the bedstead the rest of the way. Cabe stayed to help put it up, and it did look handsome after Granny had made up the bed and put her famous Flower Garden quilt on it.

"You didn't really see any bugs, did you, Cabe?" I asked, trying to unscrew one of the brass knobs.

"Naw, but it worked, didn't it."

"How'd you ever get it off? I can't budge this one."
Cabe took hold and tried to unscrew it. "I guess
it was the other one," he said. "This must be rusted
on." He kept trying, though, and finally got it loose.

"Nope, not nary a bug," Cabe said, shaking the
brass knob. And then something did fall out on the
floor. He picked it up and examined it closely. "Well,
say, look at this." He began unrolling a piece of paper.

"A hundred-dollar bill!" Lou gasped, and Granny
and I reached over and touched it gingerly to see if
it was real. We hurriedly unscrewed the others, but
there were no more.

"A hundred dollars," Cabe said, softly respectful.

"Oh, Simm, Simm," Granny was crying. "You
weren't out of your head at all."

We explained to Cabe what Granny was talking
about and stayed until she had quit crying and calmed
down. Then we hurried home with the news.

Life was full and satisfying, I thought, as I paused
momentarily at the barnyard gate. The soft summer
twilight was a gentle thing. Mockingbirds were already starting their evening serenade. Chimney swifts
circled overhead. We would have to hurry with the
milking tonight. And then I saw him, chained up
in the machine shed, pawing and snorting and bellowing profanely. Dad and Grandpa were standing off,
looking at him critically.

"How'd he get here?" Lou demanded, outraged,
pointing an accusing finger at the familiar old brindled, diabolic fiend.

"We bought him," Dad said proudly. "Looks as if you kids might get to college yet."

We didn't want to seem unappreciative. Dad set a great store by a college education. Lou managed a sickly green sort of grin, and I smoothed out the goose-flesh on my arms. We, too, had thought vaguely of a college education, but now it seemed a dismal thing indeed.

"I guess we'll need it, though," Lou said glumly, "if we're going to have to cope with that bull and his offspring the rest of our lives."

## *The Psychological Approach*

OUR BARN was sturdy and roomy and comfortably cobwebby, but not the biggest one in the valley. Our cows were just placid, old, cud-chewing cows. Even the hound dogs couldn't boast a pedigreed hair on their black and tan sides. But the well! There was something a man could brag about. Something that lent stature and prestige to the whole farmstead. Eighty-five feet deep she was, through solid rock, drilled with a diamond drill!

Few relatives, friends, or strangers ever set foot in our house but what they were shortly invited to imbibe of its bright, crystal waters, hand-drawn from some mysterious subterranean depths, where, according to Grandpa, it was surely concocted and specially dispensed by some rare and gifted Neptunian servants.

Brushing aside Grandma's or Mama's more plebeian offers of a cup of tea or coffee, Grandpa, ever the genial host, would say, "Come out and have a drink of my well water," and lead the way like some old Ganymede out through the kitchen to the well porch, his moustache twitching with excitement and a gleam in his eye like one about to reveal a wonderful phenomenon.

"Steve, it isn't any more your well water than it is the rest of us," Grandma would mildly complain. But Grandpa drank more of it than the rest of us, especially while he plowed the corn, planted the wheat, and cut the hay.

"Wahhhater! Wahhhter!" There wasn't a place on the whole farm where we couldn't hear him. Even when he was working clear up in the Fifteen Acre Field. Old Stono and Simms, and mountains of lesser degree rising on either side of the valley, would catch up the stentorian demand and relay it diminishingly down the valley until it died away in one last mournful entreaty to save a dying man.

"I wish just once all the neighbors would come a-runnin' with a bucket of water," Grandma said. "Cure him of some of that tomfoolishness. A jug of water in the shade ought to keep cool till noon."

Lou and I, who had to traipse barefooted through the sweltering hot berry patches and stubble fields with the water, heartily agreed.

The well porch was a pleasant place, and Mama said Grandpa just got to thinking about it out there in the hot fields and that's what made him holler for so much water. The same roof that covered the long back porch extended over it, but you stepped up two steps, through a latticed archway which set it aside from the rest of the house. Enclosed by honeysuckle vines and old-fashioned spice roses, it was a cool, quiet little outside room, visited often by hummingbirds and honeybees. In one corner was the big well rock, six feet square! And in the exact center of this, the pump, a grayish blue-tin enclosure with a turned-down spout in front and a crank on the side.

"Works on the centrifugal principle," Grandpa had explained many times, in minute detail and at great length.

Hanging on a whitewashed corner support was the gourd dipper, a commodious affair, holding more water than the average person could consume in three ordinary drinks, but when Grandpa wanted to take a drink, he wanted to water himself all over, Grandma said. He'd pump the dipper sloppily full, hold it appreciatively out in front of him for a few seconds like he was proposing a silent toast to the world in general, then bring it drippingly to his mouth. When he didn't have his Sunday clothes on, he'd turn the dipper up so far that the water would spill out and run down the ends of his moustache and drip off on his shirt. Then, if there was any left in the dipper when he was through, and it was a hot day, he'd look at it thoughtfully for a minute, remove his sweat-stained hat and splash the water on top of his head, letting it run down behind his ears and through his bushy white eyebrows. With a loud and satisfied and protracted, "Ahhhhh," he'd carefully hang the dipper back up, mop his brow, and proceed with the day's work.

On summer nights the well porch was a mecca for the whole family. It was cool and fragrant and through the window in the honeysuckle one could see the big wagon-wheel moon roll up over the hills, softening the landscape in its silver light and making calico patterns of shade out under the cherry tree. Lou and I bounced our rubber ball against the near-by chimney, caught lightning bugs, and prodded the night toads about the dew-damp yard. From the porch came the comfortable muted talk of the grownups and the soft creaking of the rocking chairs.

Of course there was another well down at the barn, probably from the same vein of water. Certainly the water was just as clear and sparkling, once you got it. The trouble with the barn well was that you had to pump and pump and pump to get anything and then when the water did start flowing you still had to pump and pump and pump to fill the big mossy, wooden trough where the animals drank. Every day Lou and I had to fill that trough, and on Saturdays we had to pull the big wooden stopper and scrub it out with ashes and sand. And then, if you got hot and tired pumping, you were obliged to go to the house for a drink, for drinking from the barn well was forbidden. The platform of big sandstone rocks wasn't put together too snugly and it was pointed out that some holes were big enough for a cat or rabbit to fall through.

"What we need is a new pump, and all this mortared up, and a new capping rock," Grandpa had said, time after time.

"Take a hundred and fifty dollars, Steve," Grandma had always replied, in a tone that ended the matter.

Nevertheless, Grandpa thumbed through the catalogue in the pump section and one Saturday, when Lou and I were along, we went by the hardware store and had a look at the pumps.

"Need a new pump for that well, Mr. Bell?" Mr.

Barton the hardware man, jibed Grandpa. No one in the whole county had escaped Grandpa's discourse on the qualities of his well.

"For the one at the barn," Grandpa replied, cryptically. "Why don't you get your prices down to a decent amount?" he grumbled, moving from one pump to another. "Set here on your bottom all day, getting rich off of poor people without lifting your hand."

"Well, tell you what, Mr. Bell. I'll make you a good price on that pump there. It's twenty-five dollars. I'll let you have it for twenty-four-fifty."

Grandpa snorted. "By George, man, you are generous."

Whereupon Mr. Barton laughed and slapped his thigh like it was a big joke. Then in seriousness he leaned toward Grandpa and said, "Tell you where you might pick up twenty-five dollars, Mr. Bell. Even more, if you've a mind to."

Grandpa looked doubtful, like Mr. Barton might be suggesting something that smacked of the activities that went on in the back room of the livery stable.

"Oh, it's all above board, now," Mr. Barton explained, seeing Grandpa's censorous look. "Feller over to the hotel looking for a quiet place to stay this summer. Puny looking. Studying something or other. Educated man, seems like. Be a paying guest." Mr. Barton raised his eyebrows at the possibilities and Grandpa pulled at his moustache thoughtfully.

"What's he studying?" Grandpa asked.

"Don't know for sure. Has a white rat in a cage and a lot of books. Miss Abbie says he's always talking about Direct Attack or something or other. But with your big garden and your own meat and milk, be clear profit, Mr. Bell." And then, as though remembering what was in it for him, he added, "Why, you can buy this pump over here." He walked over to a larger, more expensive model.

Grandpa tried the handle, comparing the qualities of the lift pump against those of the crank type, commented on the suction mechanism, the valves, the paint job. Lou and I tried the pump, too, and thought it would be much easier than the old one we were so familiar with. And we'd never seen a white rat before!

A week later the professor arrived, bags, books, and boxes. He was a little wheezy, near-sighted man, apparently suffering from hay fever. Grandpa was on hand to greet him and, after a decent interval said, "Come out here, professor. I want you to taste my well water."

The professor followed like an obedient child, sneezing and wiping his nose, but after he had taken a generous drink, reflected on it a while, and taken another one mincingly, he pronounced it, in a matter-of-fact but conclusive tone, "Flat."

"Flat?" Grandpa demanded, incredulously.

"Yessir. Flat," the professor replied, and there being nothing else to say, made his way, unescorted, back to his room, leaving Grandpa standing there holding the dipper, his moustache moving up and down with unuttered words.

The professor didn't set too well with Mom and Grandma either. After coming down for breakfast an hour or two after the family had eaten and just when Grandma had the churning started, or Mama some bean canning, he'd want someone to listen to his dissertation on the Dangers of Defense Mechanisms.

"Too many other mechanisms out of fix around here for us to listen to that," Grandma would say, guardedly, and remind Lou and me we'd better get started on the pumping for the livestock.

"Now, you take the haphazard way you live around here," the professor said one day, tactlessly. "You waste too much time and effort by lazy behavior patterns." Grandma and Mama exchanged secretive looks of outrage. "For example," he cast his eyes around searching for a suitable example. "Well, for example, I've noticed you've been trying to break up some broody old hens. I bet you've been wandering around in the same blind alley for years. First you doused them in a bucket of cold water, didn't you? Then you tied long strings to their legs? Now I see you've got them in a small coop. And in the end how do you break them?"

"Why, I guess I cut their heads off and cook them," Mom said, a little ruefully, because she had never won in this battle of broody hens.

"Exactly," the professor said triumphantly. "Now, if you'd do that in the first place, think of the time and effort you'd save for other problems."

"What other problems?" Mom asked blankly.

"But it's the Behavior Pattern!" The professor all but stamped his foot.

And then it was Conditioned Responses, Associative Learning, Psychoanalytic Techniques, until Mom declared we'd all be full-blown "skillet fiends," or whatever it was he called 'em.

"I wish he hadn't paid his board in advance and that Steve hadn't already spent it on that new pump," Grandma said, wearily, as time went on. "Then we could just more or less ask him to leave. That would be the 'Direct Attack' method, wouldn't it, he's always talking about?" She and Mom were learning a lot of psychology.

"I'd almost be willing to take it out of the interest money and refund it to him," Mama threatened. "Lazy behavior patterns, indeed. I'll try his Direct Attack method and see how he likes it."

We had fried chicken, baked chicken, chicken fricassee, chicken aspic, chicken ad infinitum. But the professor never complained. He liked chicken.

Lou and I were the only ones enjoying the benefits of the professor. After the new pump was installed we could fill the trough in five minutes. "And look at the time we've got left for other problems!" Lou teased Mom.

This extra time was usually spent watching the white rat the professor kept in some sort of wire maze out in the back yard.

"You observe, now," he would say, "that he has learned not to go that way after the cheese because this battery contraption here will give him a shock. Soon he will learn there is fine wire across this opening and he will avoid that. One of the main differences between mice and men is that it takes one longer to figure things out than the other." Then, just as we were getting real interested in the rat, Grandpa would holler, "Wahhhater. Wahhhater!"

"Do you know any way of stopping Grandpa from hollering that?" I asked the professor.

"Yes," he acknowledged, modestly. "Power of Suggestion, you know. Might be an interesting project."

At the dinner table the next day, the professor asked that water from the spring be used for his coffee and drinking water. This just added another maze to our runs, for now we not only had to carry water to Grandpa, but water from the spring especially for the professor. But we were patient and observant. Rome wasn't built in a day, the professor reminded us.

He'd go out to the well now with Grandpa, pump himself a big drink, bring it to his lips, stop and sniff, then throw the water away like he wasn't thirsty after all. Other times he would adjust his bifocals and peer down into the dipper, and as if having his suspicions confirmed, dash it out through the honeysuckle vines.

"There isn't anything really in that water, is there?" Lou demanded when we had the professor alone.

"No, but there *could* be," he said, in a manner obviating himself of all intrigue.

At such times when the professor was wordlessly condemning the water, Grandpa would look like someone had slapped him in the face and would cut his own drink short. And then, when he thought no one was watching, he'd sniff at the water himself and peer into the dipper.

On Sunday, after the professor had started this project about the water, Uncle Ed and Aunt Grace came out for a visit. Grandpa never once offered to take them out for a good cold drink.

"What's the matter with Pa?" Uncle Ed asked Grandma later in the day. "Seems to be in low spirits about something."

"Matter enough," Grandma said, her eyes flashing. "This so-called professor and his white rat we got here has just about knocked the props out from under him. You know how proud he's always been about the well. Seems like it's sort of sustained him. Well, he doesn't seem to enjoy it any more. Won't even sit out there with us in the evening."

"Well, I never thought Pa would let anyone get next to him like that."

"Neither did I, but the children say he doesn't even holler for water from the fields more'n once a day. Course I always thought he overdid that a little, but he looks plumb tuckered out when he comes in at noon now."

Lou and I didn't like it either. We had more time to watch the white rat but we kept straining our ears to hear Grandpa's familiar call and were a little sorry we'd asked the professor to stop it. We even took Grandpa a bucket of water one day when he hadn't called for it, but instead of sloshing what was left over his head, he dashed it at the horses.

It made our personalities split. We were glad to get out of so much water carrying, but yet we felt sorry for Grandpa. He had a hurt look, like a hound pup that had just been kicked and expected to be kicked again.

"We did it," Lou confessed to Grandma one day when she was discussing Grandpa's malady with Mom. "We had the professor use his Power of Suggestion."

"What's that?" Grandma demanded suspiciously. "I thought he had something besides hay fever."

"Oh, it's just doing things and saying things that gets someone to believing like you want them to, so he says."

"You don't say?" Grandma said, and went out to ponder the white rat a while, muttering, "Maybe this works both ways."

At supper that evening, Grandma helped herself to the green beans, took a bite, tasted inquiringly, took the bowl and set it off the table. Next morning she peered into the jelly glass and quietly removed it.

"That pork taste all right to you?" she asked the rest of us at the dinner table. We thought it did, but not being satisfied, she got up and inspected the glass jar from which it had come.

"I tell you," she said from time to time, "if we don't get rid of the mice around here I don't know what we're going to do.

"Whew, wild onions in that butter," she announced, sniffing around her churn. All this went on while the professor was at hand.

The professor started losing weight with so much *tainted* food and Grandma winked at the white rat. Then came the master stroke.

" 'Bout time we started sending Uncle Matt his water," she remarked one day after a conspiratorial conference with the rest of us. "Suffers with hay fever, you know," she informed the professor. "Loses weight." She clucked her tongue sadly. "Only thing that keeps him going 'long 'bout this time of the year is water from our well. He swears by it. Says it keeps up his appetite. I think it's just a mental quirk, don't you, professor?"

"Could be," the professor smiled tolerantly, wiping his eyes and nose.

"Course you notice how healthy we all are," Grandma added. "Say, you look a little green around the gills. Why don't you try it again?"

We left off the spring water first and nothing was said. Then Mama and Grandma began telling the professor how much better his hay fever was getting.

"You really think so? Kerchoo!" he asked, wiping his bifocals abstractedly.

"Oh, it's noticeable," Grandma remarked. "And your appetite's picking up, too."

Then one day Grandpa caught the professor out at the well drinking from the gourd dipper. "Guess it's all in getting used to it," he told Grandpa. "Don't seem so flat as at first."

The very next day came the familiar call from the field, "Wahhhater! Wahhhater!"

Everything was working out just fine. Grandpa's pride in his well was restored. The new pump at the barn was a wonderful labor saver, and all paid for, and the professor was leaving.

"I can't tell you how much I appreciate your letting me stay out here this summer," he said. "Through the trial and error process, I feel that I've at last found the kind of life I like. And I'd like to leave the white rat for the children. I think it will be good for them to continue the study. If one could get off in early life to the right approach, not relying on Defense Mechanisms or rationalizing, it makes for a happier life. And in return I'd like to ask a little favor of them." He turned to us. "Would you be so kind as to ship me five gallons of the water every week same as you do your Uncle Matt?"

"But we don't—" I began, and found Lou's elbow in my side.

"We'd be glad to," she assured the professor.

Now, instead of hearing Grandpa's lusty call from the fields, the distant freight trains seemed to whistle, "Wahhhhhhhater. Wahhhhhhhhhhhater," and very dutifully on each Saturday we took a can of crystal water, hand-drawn from some mysterious subterranean depth, to the station to be shipped to the professor, and picked up the returning can.

We moved the white rat to the barn and it was more and more of a chore to feed him, though we did this dutifully, too, throwing the food into the block at the far corner of the cage and leaving him alone to wander his way to it.

"The hair-brained numbskull," Lou murmured one day. Seemed like all of our troubles were tied up with that rat.

"Look," I said. "He went directly to it that time." We stared in amazement. The next day he did the same thing and the day after that.

"Well, what do you know, he really did learn," Lou said. "Still seems like a hair-brained numbskull to take him so long, though. I wonder what it was the professor wanted us to learn from him?"

"Search me," I replied. "He was always pointing out that humans were so much smarter than rats, that it wouldn't take them so long to figure out something."

"Well, are we humans or rats?" Lou asked, looking off into space. "Yeah," she said slowly, as if answering her own question. "Get some paper and pencil," she demanded.

I hastened after the required articles and sat patiently while she made her notes or whatever it was she was writing. When she was through she handed it to me.

*Dear Professor:*

The white rat got loose and may have fallen into the well. Therefore, we know you don't want any more water. Thanks for letting us have him. We have learned a lot.

Kind regards,<br>Lou

"But he didn't fall in the well," I protested.

"Well, he *could* have," Lou said, sounding just like the professor. She reached over and opened the door to the cage.

# The Blue-Checked Linoleum

SOMETIMES we went into a regular orgy of "fixin'
up the place," small areas at a time. Grandpa
traded a neighbor out of a glass doorknob and put it
on the inside kitchen door where none had been for
a long time. It looked so pretty Grandma said she
just believed she'd knit a new rag rug. Mama made
some new flour-sack curtains. Lillian began keeping
a scrapbook of pictures of pretty kitchens so that when
she got to teaching school some of the ideas could be
adapted. Daddy made a flower box for the cabinet
"window." Lou and I wanted to contribute something, too.

"Embroidered dishtowels?" I suggested and crum-
pled beneath her withering look. Some people are
born with a broader scope than others.

"A linoleum!" she announced.

"Hah!" I replied, "the Gettysburg Address money
is all gone."

Linoleum, linoleum, linoleum! We did a regular
thesis on linoleums. We studied those of our neighbors, those at Wallingford's Mercantile, and those in
the catalogue. I could close my eyes and see every
linoleum offered and quote the prices, too. The cheap-

est was twelve dollars and ninety-eight cents. And this
was just a nine by twelve, too. Our kitchen would
take two of this size. The only good that came of
all our research, as I saw it, was that I won the spell-
ing match one Friday at school, turning the side down
on "linoleum."

We discussed the matter hopefully with Lillian, for
all her scrapbook pictures had linoleums, and she did
say that if and when she got the school she would
see about it. She wanted to teach the district school
as badly as we wanted the linoleums. But this was a
vague, long-term, inadequate proposition, we felt.

And then, just like turning to the back of the book
and finding the answer, there was an ad on the back
of our next month's magazine: "Linoleum—9x12—
only $1.98." In big type it proclaimed the glad tidings
and showed the linoleum in color. Big blue- and
cream-colored blocks, the very shade of the Blue Willow bean jar. The utter simplicity of it astounded us.
Just hand the mailman a dollar ninety-eight, plus a
few cents shipping charges, and the thing was ours—
for keeps. No more Saturday morning scrubbing and
scouring of the plank floor. Why, at that price we
could get two and cover the whole room. One in
my name and one in Lou's. That would take four
dollars, approximately. I had a quarter. Lou had a
dime. That left only three dollars and sixty-five cents.
Patched feed sacks we could sell at the Farm Bureau
for a nickel each. That would take—ummm-ummm—
we calculated rapidly, Lou drumming on her forehead
and I counting on my fingers—seventy-three bags!

Off to the feed room we sailed. Two, four, nine—

twenty-five holey bags we had.  One dollar and twenty-
five cents.  Not enough.

"Wonder what Staceys do with theirs?" Lou pondered.

"And Ritters?" I added.  Our voices were ragged
with anticipatory delight.

"We can't just come plain out and ask for them,"
I said on the way.

"Of course not, silly.  We'll patch on shares."

"One for two?"

"One for one," Lou said firmly in her hard-bargain
voice, her jaw set in stern lines.

Staceys had only thirty sacks, which netted us fifteen.
Ritters had forty-seven and we allowed them the extra
one, claiming twenty-three for ourselves.  That left us
ten bags short.  We went all the way down to Mc-
Farlands only to find they didn't have any.  But a mile
on down the river at Crawfords, we contracted for the
additional twenty sacks needed.

We garnered these sacks secretly, caching them in
the corncrib and later smuggling them up to the attic
where, with darning needles and twine string, we em-
barked on our financial coup, which was far better
than selling Ease-All, we told each other.

"Say, what are we going to patch with?" I asked,
scissors poised.  We had always cut up an old sack
before for patches, but we were operating on too
small a margin for that.  Why, it would take at least
ten sacks for patches!

We searched the barn, chicken house, blacksmith
shop, smokehouse and attic for suitable patching ma-
terial but found none.  We didn't dare use up the

quilt scraps. So we were delayed three weeks longer until we and our neighbors had collected a few more sacks and the mice had done their part about the holes.

We were often questioned by members of the family as to the amount of time we were spending in the attic these days and came to intersperse our patching with suitable sounds of playing which drifted down to the kitchen through the hole in the ceiling.

After many needle jabs, yards and yards of twine string, a thousand knots, and countless patches, we were finished. Patched sacks were delivered to the neighbors and we rode atop our own bundle in the bed of the big wagon to the Farm Bureau store. In our pockets were the precious orders for the linoleums, and as soon as we had received our money we rushed to the post office and mailed them.

What agony to be so proud of oneself and not be able to tell about it for the two whole weeks it took the linoleums to come.

We rode to town with Grandpa again in the big wagon and collected our wonderful cargo at the depot. Grandpa looked at the labels unbelievingly and was reluctant to put the linoleums in the wagon, but we assured him they were all paid for and were just a little surprise we had planned for Mama, tossing our heads lightly as if we were in the habit of doing such elegant things.

If Grandpa was reluctant to bring them home, Mama was even more reluctant to put them down. Her struggle between disbelief, surprise, and hoping that it was true, was comical. She'd back off and look at us skeptically, waiting for us to tell her how we got

them, but all we could say was that we had patched
feed sacks and sold them.

"But we wouldn't have that many bad sacks in ten
years," she protested.

"We patched on shares," Lou confessed.

"Shares?" Mom asked.

"One for one," I explained, trying to undershoot
my jaw like Lou.

When she told Dad about it that night he said,
"Why, there's not that many sacks in the whole valley."

"Well, maybe the others don't keep theirs sold up
like we do," Mama tried to reason, still clucking her
tongue and taking in the beautiful sight that was our
transformed kitchen.

When Old Tabby came rushing in for her saucer
of milk that evening she slid halfway across the kitchen before she could get her footing. Then she lifted
her feet gingerly and set them down softly with proper
respect for our accomplishment.

Aunt Hannah and Uncle Joe were our first visitors
after the linoleums. Lou met them at the door: "You
got any tacks in your shoes?" she inquired ungracious-
ly. But, after all, we felt very proprietary about the
linoleums and wanted them to last our lifetimes.

Aunt Hannah said when she got back to the city
she was going to send Mom a length of blue checked
oilcloth for the table that would just put the finishing touch to the kitchen, so we watched the mailbox
closely. One day there were letters for Lou and me
both. We didn't often get mail and were pleased to
have some of our own.

We sat down on convenient rocks and tore open our letters, which read:

*Dear Madam:*

We know that you are pleased with the merchandise recently ordered. Enclosed is a convenient self-addressed envelope for your first installment payment of $1.00. This amount is due and payable on the first of each month. If payment is not received promptly, a small interest will accrue.

**Yours truly.**

"What do they mean?" I asked, looking at Lou who was still staring at her letter.

"Search me!" She shrugged her shoulders eloquently.

"Maybe they didn't get our money," I proposed.

"Naw, they wouldn't have sent the linoleums if they hadn't," Lou said.

". . . first installment of $1.00," I reread. "What's an 'installment'?"

"That means there's something more to come," Lou replied, trouble knitting her brow.

And something more did come. The very next month there was another perplexing letter just like the first one, with a few cents interest added, just as promised, for not having received the first installment, which the company knew was just an oversight on our part.

In the same mail was our farm magazine again, and there, still on the back, was our linoleum, still offered for $1.98.

"What does that word 'down' mean?" I asked.

"I don't know. I see that a lot," Lou replied.

"Hadn't we better write them and tell them we sent the money?" I asked.

"Yeah, their address is still there isn't it?"

I scanned down through the fine print, my eyes lighting on the word 'installment.' I backed up and read it all then—the biggest belated piece of reading I ever did. I stuffed it into Lou's hands with glittering eyes and paralyzed tongue.

I watched her eyes travel down the page and saw the pupils get big and alarmed.

"It says they're fifteen dollars, doesn't it?" I asked, stumbling along backward, trying to look up into her face. "And we pay a dollar a month until they're paid for?" I hoped I was wrong.

"Wait a minute, now," Lou said, emphatically, more to the linoleum company than to me, and we sat down by the roadside and read it again.

"Well, what did they put that $1.98 up there in great big figures for?" Lou demanded, defensively.

"What'll we do?" I ventured in a small voice.

Lou looked at the warts on the back of her hand a long time. She picked up some pebbles and threw them desultorily across the road.

"Well, don't cry." She looked at me witheringly. "We'll just send the money."

*Send the money?*

"Well, money's not the hardest thing in the world to get," she said, but I thought she was whistling in the dark and three months later I was sure of it.

We gleaned a few more sacks to patch, dug bushels of May apple and sassafras roots, and sold a gallon of wild strawberries. When James Adley got the school instead of Lillian, we even took the new kittens to town and tried to sell them from door to door, first for a quarter, then a dime, and finally a nickel. We sold only two, and them for a nickel. Uncle Hayden came out one Sunday and gave us a dime apiece which we carefully hoarded in the old tobacco can we kept under the mattress. We were always a month behind and sometimes, when we couldn't raise two dollars—two dollars and fourteen cents really, counting the money orders and postage—we would go ahead and make the payment on first one and then the other. It was a sweating nightmare to be so in debt and trying to keep it from Mom and the others. We haunted the mailbox for fear one of the notices would fall into her hands. We had to save our Fourth-of-July quarters instead of getting ice cream and soda, and never again did they have a Gettysburg Address contest. We were sorely tempted at Sunday school when it came time to drop our pennies in the collection plate. Many a time I was ready to throw up my hands and quit, or at least lay the problem before Lillian, but Lou said she had her own troubles and disappointments, what with not getting the school she wanted so badly, or any school at all for that matter.

"The berries will be ripe pretty soon," Lou said, "and we've got those three hens setting. We'll be able to sell the chickens this fall to meet the payments."

We begged Dad for space in the cornfield and sold roasting ears. It wasn't so bad in the summer when you could raise things and we came to respect the good earth like we never had before and to wonder what people did, how they ever had a sense of security without the land to fall back on.

We got embarrassed asking the neighbors for sacks the minute we thought they had an empty one. Lots of times they had only good ones, too, and we didn't ask for them. We had a few shreds of ethics left, but they were getting frazzled.

"You kids going into the sack business for good?" Mr. Stacey asked one day when we stopped by to see if they had any more.

"Oh, we're just trying to raise a little money," Lou replied, struggling to muster some cheer. Mr. Stacey was president of the local school board and we didn't want to make any rash confessions that would reveal our former foolishness. It might harm Lillian's chances for the school in the future.

"Why don't you take magazine subscriptions?" Mr. Stacey asked. "Look here," he said, rummaging on the table for a magazine. "See right here on the back, it says, 'Make $50.00 or more a month selling magazines.' "

Lou and I didn't bat an eye.

"That's just to hook you," Lou said, knowledgeably.

Mr. Stacey looked at us sharply, a little glint of respect in his eye.

"You mean you don't believe it?" he demanded, only half serious.

"Oh, you could probably make fifty dollars, but read the fine print," Lou stabbed at it with her finger, "and see what it says."

"You always read the fine print?" he questioned.

"Yessir, we do now," I said, heartily.

He began laughing and patted us on the shoulders. "That's right, kids. Always read the fine print," he commended. "Be better if that new schoolteacher had read the fine print," he remarked.

We wondered what he meant by that.

"Pretty shrewd kids," we heard him say to Mrs. Stacey as we went out the door.

"Not shrewd enough," Lou said, bitterly. The strain of keeping it from the rest of the family and raising the terrible money every month was telling on us.

We struggled through the summer, a nickel here, a dime there. The chickens hadn't turned out well. Too many of them died when little. And to think we'd still be at it this time next year if the interest kept accruing. And it did.

"Do you think any of the A.T. & T. stock is in our name?" I asked Lou.

"You know what?" she said, sinking to even lower depths and dragging me along, "I think A.T. & T. stock is old Anabelle, Trudy, and Trixy!"

Then one late summer day we came into the kitchen to find Mr. Stacey there. Mom and Grandma and Lillian were all seated around the table looking seriously happy.

"So," Mr. Stacey was saying, "our fine Mr. James Adley signed two contracts, thinking he'd pick the better of the two schools. Some people will sign anything, you know. And he was held to his first contract, so we let him out of ours." He folded his glasses and put them away in the case. Lou and I drew nearer.

"Well," Mr. Stacey continued, rising, "we're mighty happy that you'll teach the school for us, young lady, at this late date." He looked at Lillian. The full import of his visit came to Lou and me in a knee-weakening flash. "You know," he said, turning to us, "I told the school board we couldn't go wrong on hiring Miss Lillian here when even these little ones have more judgment than to get involved without reading a thing. I believe they're the ones who swung the deal." He laughed heartily and Lou and I joined in even more heartily.

Neither Mom nor the others knew what he was talking about, but we enlightened Lillian a little later when we had her alone. Lou was never one not to press an advantage when she had it. And, of course, Lillian came to our rescue with her first pay check and paid off the balance without ever letting Mom know, we think.

"We ought to do something nice for Lillian," Lou said one day, thumbing through the magazine. "Here's a diamond ring we can get for just selling . . ." I flew out the door and slammed it jarringly behind me.

## *Ka'line's Country*

"KIDS HAVE it easy these days, don't they?" Uncle Hayden asked Mama. They were sitting on the well porch and I suppose Uncle Hayden had been watching Lou and me put together a jigsaw puzzle. We did have a pitcher of lemonade close by and a plate of cookies, and living looked easy.

"Well, the girls do their chores, Hayden," Mama defended.

"Chores, bah. Kids don't know what chores are these days. Why, when I was their age. . . ."

Lou looked at me across the puzzle and rolled her eyes heavenward. That very day we'd milked the cows, taken them to pasture, fed the chickens, gathered the eggs, hoed in the fields, washed and dried dishes three times, turned the separator, carried in wood, and done lots of other little odd jobs.

"Well, Hayden, chores for farm children haven't changed much since you were a kid."

"But I mean, Myrtle, they don't have any worries. They just eat and sleep, work a little and play a lot. When do kids begin to think seriously about things?"

"Time enough for that, Hayden," Mama replied.

"What is there to worry about?" Lou asked, trying a piece of the puzzle that wouldn't fit.

For answer Uncle Hayden laid his palms open appealingly and helplessly, as if daring us to say what wasn't there to worry about.

"Now, you take the price of cotton," he turned back to Mama.

"That's what I thought, Hayden. You're worried about your old cotton, aren't you?" Mama chided.

"You got cotton, Uncle Hayden?" Lou asked, surprised.

"Why, sure I got cotton, honey."

"Where?"

"Down at Cotton Landing. 'Bout a hundred miles south."

"What's it look like, growing?"

"You mean you haven't ever seen cotton growing?" he demanded of Lou and me, and turned accusingly to Mama.

"Well, corn, beans, oats, barley, wheat—they've seen all those. Why so excited about cotton? I've never seen pineapples growing either, Hayden."

"Myrtle, cotton is an important cog in the wheels of industry," Uncle Hayden explained with exaggerated patience. "Here you live within a hundred miles of it and the kids haven't even seen it growing." He struck a match violently and lit his pipe in puffing haste.

"Don't you want to see cotton growing?" he asked Lou and me.

"Yeah," Lou said, sensing something interesting coming up.

"Myrtle, let me take these kids down to Cotton Landing with me next week. We can stay at Cousin Colar's. Be good for 'em. Broaden their education. Kids have to take over someday, you know."

"Oh, Hayd, you get carried away with yourself. It'd be a nice trip, but you wouldn't want to bother like that."

"Well, I wouldn't have suggested it if I didn't want to bother."

"No, he wouldn't," Lou said, handing Uncle Hayden a glass of lemonade.

Mama looked at us a minute. "You really want to go?" she asked.

"Yeah," Lou said. "We ought to see cotton growin'. Broaden our education."

It was the first time we'd been so far south, and only about the third or fourth time we'd ever seen Cousin Colar and his wife Becky. The land was flat and uninteresting, we thought. The houses were either enormously big pretty ones or unpainted shacks. And they didn't work in the fields in twos or threes like we did at home, but dozens of them at the same time, some white, some Negroes.

"So that's cotton?" Lou asked, looking down the long rows of green plants. Uncle Hayden and Cousin Colar had driven us out to the fields the very afternoon of our arrival. "Where's the cotton?"

Cousin Colar laughingly explained that it came later in the fall, the actual cotton that is, and maybe we could come back then, but to get out now and examine it and play around a while if we wanted to. He and

Uncle Hayden went off to examine the work of the field laborers.

In no time at all we had seen cotton growing and didn't know what to do with ourselves. The folks working in the field yelled to us, did we want a hoe?

We shrank back and sat down in the shade of a tree. Hoes we'd had too much of.

"Do you like it?" Lou asked, letting her eyes sweep the surrounding countryside.

"Not much," I replied, honestly. The tree we were sitting under was the only one for miles and the fields were so big. It made me tired just looking at them and thinking how long it would take me to get to the end of it and back.

Far down the lane we saw a little girl coming with a bucket of water and felt a strange fellowship for her, for many such buckets of water had we carried.

"She won't have any left time she gets here," Lou said, and I saw, too, that it was slopping out with her peculiar run-a-step-jump-a-step-hop-a-step gait.

"Hurry on here with that water, Lynchie Sal," someone yelled from the field.

For answer Lynchie Sal turned the bucket up and let it all spill out at her feet. She stuck her tongue out at the man and wiggled her hands at her ears.

"Why, you little devil. I'll beat the livin' daylights out of you for that! The man picked up a stick and started toward Lynchie Sal. She beat it down the road, leaving a cloud of dust behind her. A few minutes later we saw her coming back with another bucket full. The workers were at the other end of the field now, so she set it down at the end of the row and came hop-skip-jumping back out to the road. When she saw Lou and me, she stopped, surprised, and stared long and hard.

"Hi," she tried, experimentally.

"Hi, Lynchie Sal," Lou replied.

"My name ain't Lynchie Sal," she said. She stomped her bare foot, raising a cloud of dust, doubled up her small bony fists and advanced toward us.

"That's what they called you."

"They calls me lots of things. But my real name is Ka'line. That's what you can call me. Ka'line." She paused a minute to give us a chance to call her "Ka'line."

"We won't be here long," Lou explained.

"Oh, that's too bad. I was just a-fixin' to ast you all to come up to my house for suppah. We're gonna have fried chicken, biscuits and gravy, sweet 'tatahs, mashed 'tatahs, peas, baked beans, tu'nips, slaw, lettuce, ice cream, strawberries and chocolate cake." She paused for breath. "And soda water and candy and pork chops."

"All that?" Lou asked.

"Oh, sure. We always eats well."

Lynchie Sal strummed on an imaginary instrument and did a little dance in the dusty road, favoring an apparently sore toe.

"Where do you live?" Lou asked.

Lynchie Sal looked around as if to orient herself. Then she pointed up the lane to a pretty, big, white two-story house. It had a big porch with roses winding around the posts.

"I guess I'd better be gittin' 'long now."

She walked a little ways up the road, kicking dust with her good foot, turning every once in a while to see if we were watching. She shaded her eyes at the lowering sun and decided she might have a little more time after all, so she wandered back.

"You all know how to make geese fly?"

"Is it a joke?" Lou asked.

"Get behind them with a stick?" I guessed.

"Naw, I mean barbed-wire geese."

"Barbed-wire geese?" we demanded together.

"Come here," Lynchie Sal said. She led us out into the lane and over to the path that ran close alongside the barbed-wire fence. "Now, you just walk 'long like you was a-goin' to suppah, see? But you turn your head like this, squinch up your eyeballs and look sideways out of 'em at a row of barbed wire and before long you'll see geese flyin'." Lynchie Sal demonstrated the method.

"Lou and I both tried it but we couldn't see anything but barbed wire going by.

"Keep tryin'," Lynchie Sal advised. "I couldn't do it at first when my old man first showed me."

We kept trying but still got just barbed wire.

"Maybe your old man could show us," Lou suggested.

Lynchie Sal picked up a stick and whacked hard at a fence post. "He's daid."

"What from?" I asked. "Flu?"

Lynchie Sal turned on me in a blaze of fury and I stepped back hurriedly. "He's just daid. That's all. Just daid." Again her fists were doubled up in anger. "Now, if you all will excuse me, Ka'line will have to go to suppah. I reckon we'll have barbecued spareribs, too."

We watched her go up the lane and around to the back of the big white house.

Uncle Hayden and Cousin Colar weren't ready to go yet so Lou and I tried the geese again, but still all we saw was wire.

"She's nuts," said Lou, dismissing the subject.

Cousin Becky had a good supper waiting for us and we were hungry after our long day. Afterwards we sat out on the porch. Uncle Hayden and Cousin Colar talked about cotton prices and the cost of labor. Help had been a little fractious since the trouble last summer, Cousin Colar said.

"Did that all blow over?" Uncle Hayden asked.

"So far as I know," Cousin Colar said. "Widow and kid still around here, though, and it keeps things stirred."

"Ought never to have been," Uncle Hayden said.

"No, shouldn't have," Cousin Colar agreed. "They should have let the law handle it."

They smoked their pipes. Cousin Becky asked Lou and me what Mama and Grandma were doing at home and soon we all went to bed.

We came back out to the fields again the next day and watched the workers a while. Lynchie Sal was hop-skip and jumping along the lane with her bucket of water and we went back to our shade tree.

"Hi, Ka'line. I didn't think you'd be around after that supper you had last night," Lou said.

"Boy, was that a suppah." Lynchie Sal licked her lips and patted her stomach.

"What you going to have for supper tonight?" Lou asked.

"Oh, I 'specks we'll have fried chicken, biscuits and gravy, sweet 'tatahs, mashed 'tatahs, peas, baked beans, tu'nips, slaw, lettuce, ice cream, strawberries and chocolate cake."

"Looks like you'd get fat," Lou said.

"Oh, we just natcherly runs to thin in our family. You all want to play geese?"

Having nothing else to do we tried it again.

"Let's see how you all squinch your eyes," Lynchie Sal said, and observed our eyes at close range. "Do 'em like this." She closed her big dark eyes almost all the way. "And make the wire seem far away." She walked along the fence. "I got 'em already," she giggled. "Boy, are they flyin' high today. I 'specks we'll get all the way down to New York today."

"Up," Lou corrected.

"Up," Lynchie Sal said, as if directions were of the least importance. "We'll get all the way up to New York and we'll have dinner in one of the big 'partment stores. Just walk off and leave the dishes. Go out to the zoo. Eat ice cream, peanuts, popcorn. Get soda water and chocolate cake." Lynchie Sal kept going on up the fence out of our hearing. Soon she came back. "We made it," she said, giggling.

"Made what?"

"New York."

"Pooh," Lou commented.

"Why, that's right," Lynchie said. "Them old black devils'll take you anywhere's you want to go." She laughed affectionately, patting the barbed wire. "Why,

I 'specks I could go all the way to Africa with them.
What's the matter with you'ns?"

"That's not nice," Lou said. She meant about the
"devils."

"What's not nice? Going to Africa? Shucks, I been
farther away than that. I been all the way to Deetroit
on the back of them old black devils. It was in Deetroit"—Lynchie Sal furrowed her forehead in mem-
ory—"it was there where we had peach cobblah with
pink whipped cream, and. . . ." She spied the mail
carrier down at the end of the lane and her eyes grew
excited. "Ka'line must go see if her banjo has come,"
she said, running down the lane. She fell once and
limped a little ways before resuming her running.

We played a game of hull-gull until she got back.

"Didn't come?" Lou asked.

"Naw. They is as slow as the seven-year itch. It
must have been a yeah since I sent off for that banjo."

"Can you play one?" I asked, thinking of the one
we'd gotten for selling salve once and never could
play in spite of the ten easy lessons included.

"Can Ka'line play?" Lynchie Sal rolled her big
eyes. "Honey, you all just ain't heeard banjo music
'til you hears Ka'line play." She strummed her imaginary instrument, did a jig dance to accompany it, and
fell panting in the dust. She laid there a few minutes,
covering her face with her hands. We thought maybe
she was going to sleep right there in the middle of
the road.

"Lynchie Sal!" someone hollered from the field.
"Get up out of that dust and fetch some water."

Lynchie Sal stirred, raised to a sitting position, stuck her tongue out at the big man.

"Why, you little black devil," he said and started toward us. Lou and I shrank back and Lynchie scampered on down the road, stumbling, falling, getting up, stumbling again.

"Who is that man?" we asked Lynchie when she came loitering back up the lane, slopping her water and watching her geese.

"Who? That big black devil? Don't let him scare you none. He ain't fit to run company with a yaller egg-suckin' dog." She spat in his direction. "What you eatin'?"

"Candy. Want some?" Lou offered her what was left of her chocolate bar. Mine was already gone.

"I'm really not hungry." Lynchie took the bar and stuck it all in her mouth at once. "Ka'line had scrambled eggs and bacon, biscuits, cornflakes, butter, waffles, coffee, strawberries and chocolate cake for breakfast, so I'm really not hungry." The candy went down with a noisy sound.

"Lynchie Sal. C'mon here with that water," someone called from the field.

Lynchie Sal stomped her foot in the dust. Tears of frustration spilled down her dusty cheeks. She started to pour the water out again but Lou caught the bucket in time.

"You'll just have to go get it again, Ka'line. Why don't you take the man the water? What difference does it make what they call you? Then you'll have more time to play with the geese."

"Oh, I plays with the geese goin' and comin' with

the water." She smiled broadly, her white teeth gleaming, but she set the bucket over the fence where the workers could get it.

"I got a whippin' this mornin'," Lynchie said.

"What for?"

"I broke one of Mama's Have-a-line dishes. Boy, it went into a hundred million pieces. You should have just saw it flyin' all over the floor." Lynchie Sal giggled. "Then I come out here and hops on these old geese and I say, 'Now listen, you old black devils, I want you to take me to a land where dishes don't break, you hear,' and they took me there, too, and I had the best time with Have-a-line china, throwin' it around ever' which aways and it wouldn't break at all. I'd stayed there, too, but we's havin' oysters for suppah and I had to come back."

"Why didn't you have your oysters there where you were?" Lou asked.

Lynchie Sal giggled and looked at us sideways like she'd caught us at something, rather than us trapping her.

"Why, they was fresh out," she said. "Yessir, fresh out of oysters they was," she repeated. "Ka'line's goin' fishin' this afternoon. Want to come 'long?"

We went, and Lynchie Sal caught a snapping turtle.

"You're not going to take that thing home?" Lou demanded.

"Sure. They makes good turtle soup," Lynchie Sal assured us.

The banjo didn't come the next day or the next, or any other day we were there.

"How long ago did you order it, Ka'line?" Lou asked.

"Oh, I 'specks it was last December sometime."

"Then it's not coming," Lou assured her.

Lynchie Sal turned on us with blazing black eyes again. "You all gives up too easy. That's what's the trouble with you and your kind. If nothin' happens in a week, you gives up. That banjo'll come someday. You just wait and see." Bright tears rolled down her cheeks, leaving shiny streaks behind them.

"Well, I'm sorry, Ka'line," Lou said. "I didn't mean to make you cry."

" 'S all right," Lynchie Sal said on a big shuddering sigh.

"What you havin' for suppah?" she asked, after a while.

"Cousin Becky said she was having fried chicken cause we're leaving tomorrow," I said.

"Is that all?" Lynchie Sal demanded.

"Oh, I guess mashed potatoes and gravy and a vegetable and salad."

"She must be awful poor, not to have no more'n that."

"Well, what are you having?" Lou wanted to know. "Chocolate cake?"

"Why, sure. We always have chocolate cake."

Lynchie Sal was playing with her geese when we went down the lane in Uncle Hayden's car the next morning. We waved good-by to her and she waved back as far as we could see her. She was smiling broadly, her white teeth gleaming in the early morning sun.

"Wonder where she'll go today?" Lou said.

"I'd go some place where they'd call me Ka'line, wouldn't you?" I asked Lou.

"Silly," she replied.


"Well, well, well, and did you learn all about cotton?" Mama asked, hugging us tightly like we'd been away a year.

"Yeah, we learned all about cotton, except we didn't see any cotton," Lou said.

Mama looked puzzled and Uncle Hayden explained that what we had expected to see, he guessed, was the cotton bolls, after they'd opened. "But we'll go back in the fall," he assured us, "and you can see it then."

It was good to be home after a week away. We ran to see old Anabelle, Trudy, and Trixy to find out if they'd still know us. Driving them down the lane to the pasture seemed fun now instead of a chore.

Vacation days slid by lazily. We often talked of Lynchie Sal and wondered whether or not the banjo had come and where she had been that day on her B.B.D.'s We weren't allowed to talk like she did, so we just used the initials.

One day Lou came running across the meadow to where I was knocking over crawdad castles. "I've got 'em. I've got 'em," she shouted, hopping high into the air and running on.

"Got what?" I shouted back, thinking maybe measles.

"The B.B.D.'s."

I ran to meet her.

"You've got to be the right height for the wire," she explained excitedly. "Come on up here. I'll show you. She did see geese. Lynchie Sal did." We hurried to the barbed-wire fence along the cow lane. "See," she stood up close. "The barbs are right on a line with my eyes. See if the next lower strand will do for you?"

It did. We squinched our eyes and looked sideways as we walked along and made the barbs seem far away and there they were, flying along over about the Fifteen Acre Field, in a perfect line, and all equidistance. We laughed and pirouetted in the dusty lane like Lynchie Sal had. It was the silliest thing, seeing the big old fat geese flying along!

"She was right about us giving up too soon, wasn't she?" I said.

"Yeah, I guess so," Lou replied. "Well, come on. Where you want to go?"

"I'm going to St. Louis to see Aunt Hannah and Uncle Joe," I said.

"And I'm going to Flat River to see Uncle Hayden." Lou got behind me.

"We going the same way?" I asked. St. Louis and Flat River were different directions from our cow lane.

"Why, I 'spects directions make no difference to them B.B.D.'s." Lou mimicked Lynchie Sal and patted the barbs affectionately.

We walked to the end of the lane, giggling helplessly along the way.

"I saw Aunt Hannah," I reported to Lou at the end of the lane. "She's bringing us some new dresses for school."

"And Uncle Hayden says he's sure coming out soon to take us back to see Lynchie Sal—or I mean cotton," Lou said.

The places we went that summer. To the Kimberly diamond mines in South Africa; to Holland, where we saw the tulips and windmills, and I played with the Dutch Twins for sure; to Niagara Falls and California to visit kinfolks, and to see our aunts in Texas. It was lots of fun.

"I wish we could take Lynchie Sal something when we go back," Lou said. We went through our possessions and found the old banjo.

"Let's take it to her," I suggested. "She can already play."

We wrote Uncle Hayden and told him we'd better go if we were to get back to the cotton before school would start. Mama packed our clothes. We polished the banjo and tied a big red hair ribbon around it. In a few days Uncle Hayden came and once again we were in the flat cotton country. When we turned into the familiar lane we looked for Lynchie Sal. Somehow we expected her to be where we'd left her, waving to us, white teeth gleaming.

We stayed at Cousin Beckys as short a time as we could without seeming rude, then slipped away up the road to the big white house with our precious banjo.

A white lady came to the door, which we thought was funny if Lynchie Sal lived there.

"Is Ka'line here?" Lou asked.

"Who?"

"Ka'line," Lou repeated. "The little girl that carries water."

"Carries water? My dear, the Ventrisses have lived in this house for six generations, and so far as I know no one ever carried water."

"Well. . . ." Lou looked at me for suggestions.

"Her name may have been Lynchie Sal," I said.

"Oh, you mean that one? Why, I haven't seen her around lately. She and her mother used to live over there, other side of the drainage ditch. That one broke more of my Haviland china for me."

We went in the direction the lady pointed. Neither Lou nor I discussed Lynchie Sal's lie about her home.

"Is Ka'line home?" Lou asked. The woman was taking in clothes from the clothesline.

"What you all want with her?" she demanded suspiciously.

"We got her a present." Lou held up the banjo.

"It's a banjo," I said, when the woman didn't say anything.

She looked at it for a minute more. "My Sally is daid."

"Dead?" we whispered. Lou clutched the banjo, making an awful twanging sound. I shivered involuntarily.

The woman nodded, her lips trembling. She clung to a sheet on the line and buried her head in it. "Sally always said the banjo'd come."

"What did she die from?" Lou asked in a cracked voice.

But the woman could not answer. Her thin shoulders heaved with great sobs. We laid the banjo down on the porch and tiptoed away. We passed through the cotton fields and picked some out of the bolls to dry our eyes on, hardly noticing that now it was cotton.

Near the end of our visit, Lou asked Cousin Becky if she knew the little girl they called Lynchie Sal.

"Sure, everyone knew her. She died."

"What from?" I asked.

"Doctor said it wasn't anything special. Just malnutrition."

"What's that?"

"Well, it's just not getting enough to eat, that's what it is," Cousin Colar explained. "Her ma should have known better than to try to stay here after the trouble," he told Uncle Hayden.

"What trouble?" Lou persisted.

"Her father was killed, honey," Cousin Becky explained. "Now, come on, you all. Supper is ready. I've got fried chicken and all the trimmings."

We made it all right until we got to the chocolate cake.

"What's the matter with you children?" Cousin Becky wanted to know. "You ain't eatin' none of that cake."

"We got the B.B.D.'s," Lou explained.

"What's that?" Cousin Becky asked. "Homesickness?"

"Something like it, I reckon," Lou said.

We took a few branches of cotton back home. "Maybe your teacher will like for you to give a report on cotton," Uncle Hayden suggested, "and you can sure tell them all about it now, can't you?"

"Sure can," Lou agreed.

There were a few days left after we got back home before school would start. We wandered around listlessly from house to orchard to attic, not knowing for sure what we were seeking, but hoping somehow, some way, we could put a finale on this summer that would give it a definite closing, but yet give us something to go on. Something that would not make tears come to our eyes every time we looked sideways at a barbed-wire fence.

"The trouble with us," Lou said one day, fitting a final piece into the jigsaw puzzle, "we give up too easy." She spoke slowly, feeling her way. "If we can't put things right in a week's time, we give up." She lapsed into Lynchie Sal's dialect, "I 'specks if enuf people would get on the backs of them old B.B.D.'s and fly away to a land where no one was hungry and everybody was treated right and stays there long enuf to see how good it was and how it was done, some day we might all land there."

"But it's only a game," I said, noticing Lou's serious expression.

"I know. But suppose everyone got on them old B.B.D.'s in the morning and flew away and lived all day like they were in such a land, don't you think it might come true?"

"I don't know," I said.

"Not in a week's time, now, mind you." Lou looked up at me, warningly. "Not in a week's time. It'll be a long, long trip."

"But how are people going to know about it?" I asked.

"Well, let's start with us."

We finished the puzzle and walked down to the cow lane. I thought by the way Lou's head was turned sideways she was flying with the geese again. I dared to do the same. They looked like a double line until my eyes sort of dried up.

"Where did you go?" Lou asked me when we got to the end of the lane.

"I've been to see Ka'line, and boy, can she play that banjo."

Uncle Hayden came back out to bring something of ours we'd left in the car. It was cool in the evenings on the porch so he and Mama and Dad were drinking a cup of coffee. The porch chairs creaked comfortably. Cotton prices had turned out all right after all.

Lou and I were at the other end of the porch playing an uninteresting game of dominoes. "Aw, let's quit," Lou said. Seemed as if we had a hard time finishing anything we started lately. I guess we were both wondering how we were going to get people to act like they were living in Ka'line's country, without seeming silly to them.

"Grown people have it easy, don't they?" Lou observed, looking at Mama and Dad and Uncle Hayden. "I wonder how old you have to be before things don't bother you any more?" she asked, wistfully.

This seemed to make the whole thing come full circle since it had started with Uncle Hayden thinking we had it easy. But it was Grandma who finally put a proper finale on the summer. Not only had Ka'line died but old Mr. Scroggins passed on, too. We missed hearing his ax ring out and seeing him pass along the old woods roads.

"I'm glad I used the silver spoon for his tea," I

told Grandma one day as we sat under the Maiden
Blush apple tree. This was one of Grandma's favorite places. On long, lazy, late-summer afternoons she
would tie on a big, white, starched apron, get out
her basket of quilt scraps, and head for the orchard.
If she wanted solitude, she seldom got it for I usually trailed along. There might be such a thing as a
peppermint hiding in the bottom of her basket!

Grandma would find a comfortable spot to sit and
soon the click of needle against thimble would blend
in with other busy sounds: insects droning, the chickens clucking up in the barnyard, birds singing in the
maple grove. Sometimes an apple would fall with a
soft plop in the thick grass and wasps and bees would
swarm to tunnel in for sweetness.

The orchard fell away gently toward the pasture
where we could see the cows lying placidly in the
shade of the river trees. Then came the fields, rising
toward the hills that folded into each other—higher
and higher, blue deepening to indigo and then purple.

"Grandma, do you think that when I enter into
eternity that I will meet Ka'line and Mr. Scroggins?"

"Possibly. But nobody can *enter* eternity."

"Can't enter eternity? What do you mean, Grandma?"

She took off her glasses and wiped them thoughtfully. "Eternity began a long time ago. No one can
say for sure how long; but for a starting point let's
say it began on the first page of Genesis. You know
about that, don't you?"

I nodded, reciting. " 'In the beginning God created
the heaven and the earth.' "

"That's right," Grandma said. "Heaven and earth, and all of time. That's eternity."

She sewed a couple more patches together. Then— "Look," she said, pointing. "There's the barn lot up there. Here, next to it, is the orchard; and there, over the fence, are the pastures and fields and hills. Let's say the barn lot is that part of eternity which was here before you were even born. This orchard is the part where you are now. The pasture and fields, and those high, mysterious-looking mountains—let's say they're the part of eternity you'll learn about when you leave the orchard. It's all connected, see?"

I thought this over. "But, Grandma, that means we're in eternity now!"

"Exactly!" She was pleased at my logic. I got a peppermint for it.

That night for supper I put the silver spoon at Grandma's place. No one asked why, but Grandma looked at me and smiled.

## Uncle Joe and the Pulley

UNCLE JOE and Aunt Hannah came down to the farm almost once a month during the spring and summer, or "as long as the roads could be counted on," Uncle Joe would be sure to add in mild derision of the rough, rutty, circuitous course it was necessary to follow to get to our farm.

He was always running down the farm like that in an attempt to get Grandpa and Grandma to move to the city like he and Aunt Hannah had done some years before.

"Ain't no use you stayin' down here, workin' from sunup to sundown no longer, Steve," he would say. "Thing to do is buy that house that's for sale next to me and sit out on the porch and take things easy for a while."

Grandpa never could carry on a snappy argument, or perhaps he found his slow thought-out answers more effective. Anyway, he'd fill his pipe with elaborate deliberation, take a few puffs, twist the ends of his moustache a while and then allow that when he was ready to go to jail he'd just wait for the sheriff to come and get him. Uncle Joe said he guessed Grandpa was safe enough. Lord knows nobody but him and Aunt Hannah'd be crazy enough to come over those roads after anybody.

"Not unless they could smell one of Ma's dewberry cobblers a-bakin' through all the smoke and fumes of the city like some folks seem to," Grandpa would counter drily, a twinkle in his old blue eyes.

It was an unsolved mystery to Uncle Joe and Aunt Hannah how Grandma, never knowing for sure whether they were coming, was always just pulling their favorite, dewberry cobbler out of the oven when they arrived. They didn't know that on Saturday mornings, the time they usually set for their visits, Grandma stationed me out in the yard to listen for someone crossing the bridge five miles below the house. The valley acted as a huge megaphone for noises up and down the river. After hearing the clappity-clap of the old bridge we could count on it being nearly a half hour before Uncle Joe arrived, if it was him, and it usually was, for the road wound leisurely in and about and over the mountains as if whoever laid it out was in no hurry and didn't want to miss the view from any place. The last few miles were really rugged and Uncle Joe often threatened to leave his car at the bridge and come up the river in a canoe. "Save time, tires, and temper," he'd grumble, crawling stiffly out of their modest coupé, stretching his legs exaggeratedly and brushing over-vigorously at Aunt Hannah's calicos.

By the time they had arrived Grandma and Mama would have the best crocheted antimacassars on the parlor chairs, a fresh bouquet of flowers on the table, white, stiffly starched dimity aprons for themselves, and the smell of dewberry cobbler permeating every room of the house. Grandpa would be sitting out on the porch looking for all the world like a retired Southern colonel.

"I declare, Josie, don't tell me that's another dewberry cobbler I smell," Aunt Hannah would say.

"Oh, pshaw, 't ain't nothin'," Grandma would shrug modestly. "Sit down, Hannah. My land, you must be tired after that long drive. Jeanie, you run down cellar and bring up that pitcher of buttermilk. Wouldn't you like a drink to cool off, Joe?"

"It'd take the whole cellar to cool me off, Josie. Danged if it don't get hotter out here every summer. I don't see how you stand it." Uncle Joe would take out his big white handkerchief and mop at his brow.

"Oh, Joe," Aunt Hannah would say reprovingly, never getting used to the perennial, good-natured wrangling between him and Grandpa, "you know it's no hotter out here than it is in town."

"No hotter!" Uncle Joe would explode. "Just look at the heat dancin' over that meadow down there. I never see anything like that in town."

"I understand," Grandpa would say in his best professorial voice, motioning Uncle Joe to a chair at the shady end of the porch, "that you have to be able to see a little ways off before you can see the heat haze."

Uncle Joe would be too busy with his buttermilk to have heard.

Things went on like that for years, Uncle Joe never missing a chance to point out all the defects. Maybe it was the bugs eating up the potato vines, or the river flooding the bottom land, or the butter tasting like wild onions. The truth was, Mama said, that she suspected that he was lonesome in the city, having moved there from our friendly valley where neighbors were held in proper respect and always had time to discuss the weather, the crops, or the latest moves of the government. There seemed nothing he wanted more than to have Grandpa live close by where they could spend their declining years talking over old times on the farm, or even going farther back than that to the days when they, as youths, had crossed the Cumberland Mountains into Tennessee and gone on into the wilderness of Missouri, there to remain for the balance of their days. Sensing that Uncle Joe really missed the farm, he just countered all arguments with something good—like a fishing trip across the meadow at sundown, a Sunday morning walk down the lane when the wild plum thicket was in bloom, or a trip to the maple grove.

Once Uncle Joe and Aunt Hannah came to stay a week. It was during the haying season. I didn't see how Uncle Joe could help liking it on the farm then. We were off to the hayfields in the rickety old hayrack long before dawn, the fat rumps of the horses moving lively in the early morning coolness, bobwhites calling plaintively from the fence corners, fearful of their homes, and the sweet smell of the new-mown hay heavy on the air. But still Uncle Joe complained. The hayseed got down his neck. The briars in the hay scratched at his ankles, the heat, the chiggers, and the choking dust of the hay up in the loft all came in for an airing.

Sometimes I wondered why Grandpa didn't tell

Uncle Joe to go on home if he disliked it so much. But Grandpa was far wiser in human nature than I.

One day Uncle Joe was sitting out in the shade of the tool shed watching me lead Old Bill out and back the dusty path to pull the hay up into the loft. The fascinated way he watched you'd thought he'd never helped put hay up before.

"You know, Jeanie lass," he said after a while, fanning himself with one of Grandpa's old sweat-stained straw hats, "a pulley is a wonderful gadget."

I looked at the pulley hooked on the side of the barn and reckoned as how it was, always having taken pulleys sort of for granted.

"Now, you take that load of hay in there." He pointed in through the wide doorway of the barn where Grandpa was fixing the hayfork into the load of hay. "Man's not strong enough to throw that up in the barn loft. A mule's strong enough, only he can't throw, so you take a simple little thing like a pulley for a go-between, and your problem's solved."

"Ready!" Grandpa hollered from the front of the barn, and, with a quick nod in appreciation of the pulley, I led Old Bill out again. As I passed back by Uncle Joe I heard him mumbling something about wondering if it wouldn't work on humans, too. I thought maybe Uncle Joe had gotten too hot. Certainly he wasn't the same after that. He went about with a sly look in his eyes like he was up to something and the next time they came down you could tell he was changing his tactics. He didn't throw off on the farm any more. After complimenting Grandma on her dewberry cobbler, he began talking about the

symphony orchestra they had attended the week before. "I wish you could hear it, Josie, as much as you
like good music." Then Aunt Hannah told about
the big stores where they had nothing but beautiful
handmade quilts and crocheting and fancy work. "I
guess you could show them a thing or two about
fancy quilting, eh, Josie?" Uncle Joe said. He told
about the president going to make a speech there in
the fall and the play they would have for Christmas
at the theater.

I never was very smart at figuring out things that
weren't just almost as plain as day, but I did have
this figured out. Uncle Joe was proceeding along the
principle of the pulley, as explained in our Hamilton-
Brown arithmetic. A was Grandpa, the load to be
moved; Uncle Joe was B, the mule to apply the power;
and Grandma, C, was to be the pulley for facilitating
the moving. And the way her eyes lighted up as Uncle
Joe and Aunt Hannah described, in glowing terms,
their way of life since moving to the city, it looked
as if he had the ropes rigged up right.

Each time they came down there was something
new and exciting to tell about. "I tell you, Josie,
you never saw anything as pretty as the parade they
had for the president," or "You should see the new
dresses they've got in the windows this fall. Styles are
just like they were when we were young." Uncle Joe
would rattle on about the handiness of the buses, right
in front of the house. Wasn't nothing to go to town
just any old time, shop, eat dinner, go to a movie.
Every once in a while Grandma would sigh deeply
and Grandpa would look at her wonderingly as if it

had never occurred to him that Grandma would like city life.

"And then there's the handiness of the doctor," Uncle Joe continued. "Why, Josie, what would happen, say Steve fell down the cellar stairs some time and broke his leg? Say in the wintertime. You know how the roads are." It was plain neither Grandpa nor Grandma had given that any thought.

At butchering time Uncle Joe brought Grandpa out a new-fangled pulley, a sheave pulley he called it, to help hoist the hogs.

"You see, Jeanie," he explained, "this rope passes around the sheaves in a continuous coil. You fasten this hook to the log and when you pull on this end" —he handed me the free end of the rope—"neglecting any slight obliquity of the plies of rope, this moves six times as fast as the lower block carrying the hog, and if there's no friction or other resistance, the mechanical advantage will be the same ratio of the effort to the resistance." It was plain that Uncle Joe had gone all out on the subject of pulleys.

After the last piece of meat was cut up and salted down and the last can of lard poured off, Aunt Hannah said that since the year's work was running out, she didn't see what there was to keep Grandma from going home with them for that long-promised visit.

"Oh, Hannah, I couldn't do that," Grandma protested, but with a wistful look in her eyes.

"Now, why not, Josie?"

There seemed no good reason, so Grandma said she would go, but only for a couple of weeks, mind you! "I would like to see the new quilt patterns and get a few things to work on for the grandchildren for Christmas and, Jeanie," she said to me on the sly, "I'd like to get something real nice for your Grandpa. A real surprise. Do you have any ideas?"

We discussed a new pipe, a new pair of suspenders, a new sweater, but none of those seemed quite elegant enough. "Well, I'll just look around," Grandma said, and left it at that.

The first afternoon I came home from school after Grandma was gone, I found Grandpa just walking around through the big barn, not doing anything in particular, poking his head in the wheat bin, scooping up a big handful and letting it sift slowly back; looking in on the horses; stopping by the harness room, running his hand over the smooth leather of his favorite saddle. He climbed up into the loft and looked out the little window in the back where you could see the whole farm at once, the yellow stubble fields, the green pastures, the river, the hills. It was sad seeing Grandpa standing there, just looking. I lay back in the hay and gazed up into the dim top of the barn and there was that hateful hay track with its pulleys at both ends. The way Grandpa was standing, it looked as if he were tied to one end of the rope.

"You think she'll want to move?" I blurted out.

"I don't know, lass. I don't know." Grandpa shook his head slowly and then looked at me quickly as if surprised I had read his mind. After a while he turned from the window and sat down across from me.

"Lass, why it is when a farmer comes to retire he

thinks he has to move to the city? Why can't he stay where he knows and loves things?"

I knew Grandpa didn't expect me to answer. So I just waited for him to go on. He picked up a piece of dried timothy and ran it through his fingers, spilling the seeds off in the hay.

"There's a hundred things around here I've been laying off to do and never seemed to find time for them. Just sort of putting them off until maybe it's too late. Somehow or other I've always wanted to sit out in the middle of the ripe wheat field *all night* sometime. And then there's Simms Mountain. I've never climbed it and watched the sun come up like I've always planned to do, or sat all day down in the orchard and counted the different birds I'd see and hear."

Grandpa sat there a little while longer, his forehead puckered in thought, then, "Time to milk," he said gruffly, and we climbed down and started the evening chores.

Those were the longest two weeks we ever spent. Grandpa didn't say much but I'm sure he had the same sense of impending disaster the rest of us had. Somehow all my sense of security and stability was associated with the farm and its familiar surroundings, and the thought that Grandma and Grandpa might leave was unbearable. When Uncle Joe brought Grandma home, looking so stylish in her new clothes and a peculiar new light in her eyes, my heart sank lower and lower. Before she more than got her coat off Uncle Joe kept urging her to tell Grandpa all about her visit and I made some excuse to go to the barn where I would not show my feelings. "We mustn't let on," Grandpa had cautioned, "if your Grandma wants to move. There's no denying she's worked hard all her life and if she wants a change now, nobody could be more entitled."

I sat down on the corn planter, tested the gears, and inspected the oil pots. I found old Biddy's nest in the wheat drill and stumbled over the fancy pulley Uncle Joe had given Grandpa. Somehow it had been knocked down from the wall, and I just let it lay. I went into the chicken house and saw the sack of laying mash that needed emptying into the hopper. I started scooping it in, thinking how much easier it would be if I were strong enough just to lift it up and pour it in. Then I thought of the pulley. Grudgingly I went back to the shed for it, secured the top hook to a rafter and let down the lower hook long enough to fasten well into the sack. "I guess Uncle Joe's got something," I mumbled as I began pulling on the free end of the rope. The sack raised a few inches off the floor, though it was mighty hard pulling. I pulled a little more and the sack raised another few inches. If I could just let go with both hands and grab the rope higher up, but the pulley was not fashioned to lock in place so I let go with one hand and grabbed the rope up higher, or at least that's what I meant to do. But the pulley started racing backward and the sack of feed landed squarely on my toes.

Naturally it hurt, but I wasn't as mad as I ordinarily would have been. In fact, the longer I stood there looking at that pulley the better I began to feel, although my toe was hurting something fierce. What was it Uncle Joe had said, *"Neglecting any slight obliquity and in the absence of friction. . . ."* Well, I could add something more to that now.

They were just sitting down to the dinner table when I got back to the house.

"Why, Jeanie, where did you run off to?" Grandma asked. "Tell me, how have you and Grandpa made out?"

"Oh, all right, I guess." I looked at Grandpa to see what he had to say about it but he didn't look up.

"Now, Josie," Uncle Joe said, pulling his chair up to the table, "tell them how you like the city." He looked over at Aunt Hannah and winked and I knew something was up.

"Well," Grandma began, passing the chicken and dumplings, "it was real pretty. I guess what I noticed most was all the lights. You just never saw so many lights in your life. All colors, and all dancing and jiggling and looking like they were flying through the air. Reminded me of the lower meadow on a warm summer night when the fireflies are out. Almost as pretty, too." I wasn't sure which Grandma meant, the city lights or the meadow.

"Here, Steve, take some more chicken," Grandma said. "Why you're not eating anything. And you, Jeanie, Lou, Lillian."

"Tell 'em about the trip to the park, Josie," Uncle Joe urged.

"Oh, that was nice. Such pretty big trees and a thing they call a lagoon in the middle and a big white swan floating around on it. Not as clear as our meadow pond though, and the swan looked sort of lonesome. Wonder why they don't get some geese? It would have been a right peaceful place if there hadn't been so many people."

"Tell about the stores, Josie," Aunt Hannah interrupted.

"Why, you never saw such big stores in your life. Just anything you want right in one store. Sort of like Wallingford's Mercantile. Course they got a lot more of everything. Especially dress goods. One piece they had (I bought some of it) looked just like our upper pasture when the field daisies take over. And I got a new bedspread, Steve. It's all white and knobby. I guess I bought it cause it looks so much like the stubble field in wintertime when the snow's on." Grandma looked around a little self-consciously. "And then we went to the musical. Never saw so many people playing so many different things at one time in my life. You know, Steve"—Grandma giggled and looked apologetically at Aunt Hannah and Uncle Joe —"when I shut my eyes and just let my imagination loose, it wasn't much different from the hounds having a chase. First they were loud, then they were soft and far away, then here they came back gradually again, just like the dogs going over Simms Mountain, down the Cedar Bluffs, and back up the valley."

I could see Grandpa beginning to straighten up like great weights were falling from his shoulders. *"Almost as pretty,"* she'd said. *"Not as clear as our pond."* *"Dress goods that looked like our pasture."*

"Oh, I had a good time," Grandma kept going on, "and I do want to thank you and Hannah again, Joe, and now do you think we ought to tell them the surprise, Joe?"

"Good a time as any," Uncle Joe said, dipping deep into the mashed potatoes.

"Well, sir," Grandma paused significantly and my heart was in my throat. "Joe's going to buy the Britt farm and move back."

Grandpa just sat there staring at Uncle Joe for the longest time. I knew they were remembering lots of things, like the time when they left home to come West, the hardships they had endured together, the times of rejoicing. Their eyes grew a little dim and Aunt Hannah even took her handkerchief out and blew her nose.

I felt sort of awkward and out of place and didn't know what to say until I thought of the pulley.

"You know, Uncle Joe," I said, wishing I could sound bookish like he had. "About those pulleys. If the load you're trying to lift is too heavy for the power applied at the other end, the pulley will cause the end where the power is applied to snap backward and be drawn toward the load!" I was making a diagram with my fork on the tablecloth to demonstrate the experience I'd just had with the pulley.

Uncle Joe listened carefully and then a broad grin spread over his face and he gave me a big wink. "Yeah, they're tricky, all right. Got to watch what you're trying to move."

# The Political Fox

"THERE'LL be plenty to answer for now," Grandma glumly predicted, poking the dead fox with her toe.

"And you running for sheriff of the county!" Grandpa added, looking accusingly at Dad.

"But I tell you the dogs had him down. Don't you believe me?" Dad looked helplessly around the tight little circle on the back porch.

"In another minute they'd have had him mouthed until even the fur wouldn't have been any good." He picked up a limp paw and let it fall again. "And besides, there's no law against killing a fox."

"No law!" Grandma sputtered, looking witheringly at Dad over the top of her glasses.

"Well, no legal law yet," Dad said weakly, shuffling around.

Mom picked up the big bushy, white-tipped tail. "It's a lovely fox, Wilson. And besides, I guess there's other people in the county that vote besides fox hunters."

"Not enough," Grandma said. "If 't was me, I'd take it round behind the barn and bury it and keep our mouths shut." She looked menacingly at us kids.

Dad took the fox round behind the barn all right, but it was only to divest it of its hide. Lou and I watched from a knothole in the loft and were on hand a month later when he presented Mama with the lovely red fur piece.

"Oh, Wilson, you shouldn't have!" Mama cried, her eyes shining. "A real fur piece." She dried her hands and draped the fox around her shoulders. It did something for her. Even with her house dress on and right there in the kitchen where Grandma was churning and we were doing the dishes, it did something for her. The red of the fur caught up red tones in her dark hair. Her white skin reflected a soft flush and her blue eyes danced with happiness. I knew right then and there that being sheriff of St. Francois County didn't mean as much to Dad as seeing how Mom looked in that soft, lustrous fur.

"Better put it away until after election," Grandpa advised gloomily. " 'T ain't going to set well. Fox huntin' been gettin' poorer and poorer anyway." He adjusted his glasses and inspected the fur closely. "I 'spect that's Old Reddy, too."

Reddy was the perennial fox in the surrounding hills that could always be counted on for a good chase any night. Neighbors vowed it was the same fox the dogs chased year after year, for he'd been leading them over the same trails and back-tracking at the same places and using the same tricks, until the hunters, grouped around the campfire on top of Simms Mountain, could almost predict his exact moves.

"Well, it is too hot to wear it yet," Mom said practically, "but. . . ."

That "but" meant that the election wasn't until November and there'd be plenty of cold weather before November and she'd be blessed if she'd have something as pretty as that and not wear it. She laid the fur out on top of the chiffonier where we were allowed to stroke it and even put it on sometimes and strut around the room, humming the "St. Louis Blues," trying to look like a St. Louis woman.

By mutual but mute agreement we kept our mouths sealed in front of the neighbors. They were all old-time, dyed-in-the-wool fox hunters like us, who would rather hear a good chase than anything else in the world.

"It was sustainin', fox huntin' was," Jim Harris said. He worked and toiled in his narrow little fields all day, his mind on the coming evening when he'd take the dogs out for a little spell. A typical neighbor, Jim Harris. Lived up on top of Simms Mountain as close to the foxes as he could get.

By September, the primaries were over. Dad led his ticket, and electioneering was getting down to earnest on the porch of the Farm Bureau store and in the back of Wallingford's Mercantile. Good fox-hunting weather too—heavy dews, harvest moons, hounds ready after a long hot summer.

"Ought to go every time someone's in the notion," Dad said, as if he wouldn't anyway. "Be a wonderful place to pick up votes."

Jim Harris was always in the notion, so a few nights later Grandpa and Dad filled their lanterns, let out the hounds, and made their way across the fields and meadows and up the sides of the mountain. Mom and I climbed the hill back of the house and sat on top of the strawstack waiting for the chase to begin. We knew everyone else in the valley was listening, too—just like a big concert only the seats were miles apart.

We could hear the dogs exploring around, and once one of them got lined out like he'd hit a trail, but it ended in a few, fuzzy, weak barks, and their combined baying sounded confused and puzzled. Alexander's old Gyp, when he gave tongue, sounded like he was saying, "Wherrrrre, wherrrrre?" And the others took up the chorus, "Wheeerrrrreeeee?"

"I suspect, dear hounds," Mom answered them jokingly, "he's down on top of my chiffonier."

"But Daddy wasn't wrong in killing the fox, Mom," I protested, sliding down the strawstack after her. "He said the dogs would have got him anyway."

"Of course, he wasn't wrong, honey. But those men up there"—she motioned toward the top of the mountain—"would take a heap of convincing."

"Well, no luck last night," Dad reported at the breakfast table next morning, avoiding everyone's eyes. "But there's always another time," he said heartily.

We sat on the strawstack every night for a week, and every night it was the same thing.

"Beats all I ever saw," Jim Harris said, perplexed, when he brought down some fresh beef. "First time I recollect there hasn't been a fox in the hills since I been living here, and I've been here a mighty long time. Ain't no sign of dens nowhere. I've been out studying the hills. Person might as well give up if

he can't have the little recreation of fox hunting."
Jim looked sad.

Mom took the fur piece off the top of the chiffonier
and put it in the cedar chest.

The second week in October there was to be a big
political rally at the county seat. The governor was
coming down and several other prominent party lead-
ers. The candidates were all supposed to be there to
say a few words and, of course, the candidates wives,
to lend a little grace to the occasion. We girls got to
go, too. If things lasted too late, we could go over to
Aunt Grace's and go to bed.

We stopped by her house first on the night of
the rally, and she combed Mama's hair again and
arranged the little curls over her ears and around her
forehead and made her put on her little turquoise
earbobs.

"Oh, Grace," Mom scoffed. " 'T ain't me they'll be
looking at. Get Wilson in here and brush his suit."

Aunt Grace snorted. "You don't know anything
about politics, Myrtle. Women have more say-so than
just their votes. Why, every woman out there tonight
will be going over you with a fine-tooth comb, looking
for flaws, especially the opposition. Though I don't
know where they'll find them," she said, stepping back
and surveying Mom. "Why didn't you wear your fur?
It'd look pretty with that blue suit."

"I brought it along. It's outside. Don't you think
it's a little hot yet?" Mom asked hesitantly.

"Oh, bosh! Run and get it, Jeanie," Aunt Grace
motioned to me.

"You know, Grace," Mom said, "nobody around

home knows about the fur. Course I know it's all right. Wilson wouldn't have killed the fox if it hadn't been like he said. He's too much of a fox hunter himself to up and kill a fox unless it was a mercy. But seems as if it just hasn't come handy for us to tell about it."

"Well, if you know it's all right, what else matters?" Aunt Grace asked.

"Why, that's right," Mom said, straightening up, with new light in her eyes.

They tried it first one way and then another, but any way you took it, it looked good. And Daddy just stood and stared at Mom when she came out in the living room. I know Mom was glad, now, that she was wearing it, for it sort of said, in some mute way, "I'm with you in this."

We walked from Aunt Grace's up to the courthouse. The streets were crowded and everybody stopped to shake hands with Dad. All but the neighbors, that is. Somehow it seemed kind of silly to be shaking hands with someone so familiar, whom we had just recently passed on the way to town or shouted to in their barnyards. Hands working together on a cross-cut saw, scraping hogs, pitching hay, knew more familiarity than any handshake could convey.

They spoke of the weather and asked each other if they had their wood in yet, or inquired if the winter wheat was showing a stand. No one, not even the womenfolk, asked Mom about her fur, fearing it had been borrowed for the occasion, but you could feel them looking at it. Especially Jim Harris. He just couldn't keep his eyes off it.

We moved leisurely up to the courthouse. Lots of strangers were down from the city with the governor's party. One man kept looking at Dad peculiarly and we hoped he wasn't going to start anything. Political rallies got that way sometimes.

"I've seen him someplace," Dad said, "but I can't remember where."

Then pretty soon the man detached himself from his group and came over to Dad. "Say," he said, rather loudly and looking especially at Mom, "aren't you the guy that brought a fox hide up to the tannery here a while back? This is it here, isn't it?" He pointed at the fur piece.

"Yes, sir," Dad said without flinching.

"Finest hide I ever worked with," the man kept on. "Lots of people shoot 'em up too bad, but you put the rifle shot in just the right place."

The interested circle had closed in — Jim Harris, the Ritters, Staceys, McDowells, Claytons — all staring without saying a word.

Mom's face was getting as red as the fox fur, and Dad was putting his hands into his pockets and taking them out again, fumbling with his watch fob. He turned to the neighbors. "I never did explain how this happened," he began. But just then a call came for all the candidates to come up onto the platform, and we moved away from the sea of accusing faces.

The governor spoke first, being very vehement about his party's stand. Then the representative spoke, being even more vehement, but touching on a local subject: "You all know, of course, that we are trying to pass a bill establishing a national park in the hills out west of here. I understand that this region is one of the best fox-hunting territories in the state, and it's going to be better, for the conservation men are going to release more foxes out there soon. But I just want you to know that if such a bill is passed— and I'm for it 100 per cent—it does not mean that fox hunting is forbidden, for we all know that fox hunting is that honorable sport where nothing is killed."

There were muffled sounds of agreement, and the representative quickly ended his speech. Then the county candidates were introduced, and each spoke briefly. When Daddy got up, Mom reached down and caught hold of a small hand on either side of her. I looked up for encouragement, but all I could see was the cold, glassy stare of the fox.

"Most of you know," Daddy began, "that this is my first venture in politics, that is, as a candidate. Of course, I have always followed closely the administration of our government and have voiced my approval or disapproval through our great American privilege of the vote.

"Whenever a person decides to run for office, for some reason he is behooved to go into his past and explain his actions from the time he broke the window in the little red schoolhouse up to when he missed church last week. Before I got up here tonight I was about to start explaining some of my past actions, too. I'm glad I didn't. When you go about explaining, it makes folks think there's reason for explaining. You all know me, or most of you do. You know I'm running for sheriff of this county and that it's the sheriff's duty to prevent breaches of the peace, and if you think I'm suitable for that, I'd appreciate your vote."

There was lots of clapping and Mama's eyes were soft and glittery when Dad sat down. She was proud of him. No bowing, scraping, sniveling politician here! He'd probably lose the election, but he was steadfast in his convictions. He'd done no wrong and he refused to be on the defensive.

It looked bad. Of course, some of the opposition had been there when the man from the tannery had spoken. What more could they want? A fox killer! So his wife could put on airs! Three girls coming on, too. Take three more foxes to deck them out!

Mom said Dad was right when we got back to Aunt Grace's. No use going around explaining. If your past reputation wouldn't hold up, then you didn't deserve a high office.

"Oh, Myrtle," Aunt Grace said. "You're putting politics on too high a plane. Past reputations, my eye! Why, let a high-powered orator get a hold of 'em and they can tear past reputations to shreds."

"Not our folks," Mom said staunchly. But she looked worried when Mrs. Clayton canceled her order for a Thanksgiving turkey and Mrs. Ritter called and said she couldn't serve on the Ladies Aid Committee of which Mom was chairman. Grandpa and Dad went out fox hunting several times, but there wasn't anyone else out, they reported.

"Awful dry in the woods anyway," they said, making excuses.

At the family council held around the breakfast, dinner, and supper tables, with Uncle Hayden and

Uncle Ed called in for the urban angle, we discussed Dad's situation.

"It seems to me, Wilson, it would be a smart thing to do to tell them how come you killed the fox. No one would blame a person for killing a lame fox when the dogs were on him. Humane thing to do," Uncle Hayden summed up.

Dad was adamant, though. The race for sheriff had become secondary to him. He wanted to know if these neighbors of his, whom he had helped to wrestle logs for barn building, worked with all night in the fields to get up the hay before a rain, taken over chores for when sickness abounded, would turn against him just because he hadn't explained.

"Well, it's your funeral," Uncle Ed predicted, and that's just what it seemed to be. Three days before election, fire broke out in the Little Piney. Fire in the Little Piney was a dreaded thing. Many of the farmers used the hills for grazing their hogs and live-stock. Some of them even had hogs in the hills this late in the season. It was a vital matter—no pasture-land, no livestock. And then there was Jim's house and Gus Larkey's, and Granny Weaver's. Gus's house had been burned down once from a forest fire, and neighbors chided him for building back up there. But they always dropped everything willingly and ran to help when a plume of smoke spiraled up on the mountains.

"Get up to Little Piney," Lee Stacey shouted into the party line that night, and tired farmers from miles around arose with alacrity and made their way to the ever-reddening glow riding the ridge.

By daylight the angry smoke clouds hung over the full length of Simms Mountain and were threatening Brown Mountain. Dad and Grandpa didn't come home for dinner or supper. From past experience we knew that this meant it was bad, and the womenfolk began packing up coffee and ingredients for soup and other nourishing dishes, which they took over to the Big Gate where they set up camp, and the tired, weary fire fighters came in shifts to eat and drink hurriedly.

"Worst one ever," Dad reported. "Whole north side already gone and if the wind changes our backfire strip won't hold, I'm afraid. Wood's too dry."

All night long the neighbors battled the roaring flames. They came trudging into camp, smoke-blackened, blistered, and red-eyed.

Gus and another man were sent to town for help, and by noon the next day, regular fire-fighting crews were there, but with meager equipment and few men. That night Jim Harris's house went, and that side of Simms was abandoned. The men shifted over to the west to try to keep the fire from spreading in that direction.

Then the dreaded thing happened. Early the next morning, two men, weary for lack of sleep, tired beyond human endurance and brains smoke-fuddled, were trapped behind the fire line—Jeptha Alexander and Jeem Hollister.

"We'll take the truck and go in after them, but some of you men who know the hills will have to go along," the crew foreman said.

Every man in camp stepped forward, but Dad was the first to climb onto the truck.

It was an agonizing, fear-ridden, prayer-solaced hour before they were back, clothes burned, hair singed, tires smoking, but Jeptha and Jeem had been found, and tired, rejoicing neighbors forgot there was a fire in the woods.

That night a light but sufficient rain fell and the next morning the weary fire fighters limped home to neglected chores.

The doctor came out next morning and made the rounds, dressing burns, leaving medications and what cheer he could muster.

"Poor turnout for the election, wasn't it?" he said.

*Election!* We started from our chairs.

"When?" Mama asked weakly.

"Why, yesterday."

There was a moment of silence. Then Dad, swallowing hard, asked: "Well, how'd it come out? Sheriff, I mean?"

"Well, Madison Harvey won, I heard. Close, though. You ran a good race, Mr. Bell."

Mama screwed and unscrewed the lid of the salve jar. Grandma took off her dust cap and put it back on. Dad picked at the bandages on his arm. There was too much silence.

Finally, Grandma jumped up. "Here's a fresh gingerbread I want you to leave off at the Hollisters," she said, handing the doctor the cloth-wrapped loaf. "Tell Molly some of us'll be up to help with chores this afternoon."

After he had gone we sat around glumly thinking of the election we had forgotten.

"Oh, well," Dad said, trying to cheer us up, "if the

neighbors had got in to vote, maybe it would have been different."

"Yeah, maybe so," Grandma sighed, and we knew she was thinking, as were some of the rest of us, that it could have been worse, maybe.

Mom and Lou and I went up to Hollisters in the afternoon to help out. Lou and I had been doing an awful lot of milking the past week. While we were there, other neighbors dropped in to see how Jeem was and made plans to meet at Jim Harris's that Friday to start his new cabin. No one said anything about the election.

"They forgot about it and haven't remembered it yet," Mom said on the way home, and we wondered if we would ever really know how they stood.

The next morning, while we were still eating breakfast, Jim Harris knocked loudly on the back door and shouted: "Open up, Sheriff! You're wanted in town."

"I didn't think he'd rub it in," Dad said, limping to the door.

"Morning, Sheriff," Jim greeted. "That was a close one, wasn't it?"

"I reckon you'd call it too close when it got your house, Jim," Dad said.

"No, no. I mean the election."

"Well, I haven't seen the final tabulation," Dad said tiredly, motioning Jim to a chair. "How bad was it?"

"Twenty votes," Jim replied.

"Twenty votes," Mama said softly, and Grandma repeated, "Twenty votes."

"Yessir, I stayed with them last night until the last vote was counted."

"Last night?" Dad demanded.

"Yeah, the absentees," Jim said. "That's what made the difference."

We looked around at each other wordlessly, fearing to ask what we had to know.

Jim looked at us quizzically. "You mean you all don't know yet that Wilson here won?" He looked at us astonished. "Well, bless my hounds!" He got up and shook hands with every one of us. "Yessir, it was the absentees," he repeated. "I saw we weren't going to make it in to vote when the wind shifted Monday, so when Gus went after the fire crew I had him bring out a wad of absentee ballots." Jim looked happily around at our astonished faces. "They didn't get around to counting them until last night. No one thought they'd be 100 per cent for you. That's the reason word got out that Madison had won."

Grandma threw her apron over her head, and Mama got up and busied herself around the stove. Dad just kept shaking Jim's hand without saying anything.

"Well, say," Jim said, looking around at the silent household, "they want you to come in and have your picture taken. You, too, Mrs. Bell. Be sure to wear that fox fur. It's right becomin'."

Mama's hands flew to her hair, and I wished her picture could have been taken right then to catch that light in her eyes.

"Come nigh being mine, you know," Jim went on. "I saw the hounds after that fox that morning, and I knowed he couldn't last long. I followed them up

Little Piney and down through Cedar Creek, then soon I met the dogs coming back home. I looked all over for the fox but figured he wouldn't have been any good after they'd chewed him up. Glad you happened along in time, Wilson. Hated to say anything about it, just like I know you did, but I'm glad to see him preserved."

"And he's not just mine, Jim," Mama said. "Like before, he belongs to us all. I know Amy's going to a wedding next week, so I'll leave it off with her on our way back today."

After he was gone Dad sat for a long time just saying nothing.

"Well, that proves it, doesn't it?" Mom said happily. She looked around at us kids severely, like she did when she wanted us to remember something. "Just do the right things all the time, then you'll never have to explain your actions." She hummed a little tune as she set about getting ready. "Well, come on, Wilson. You've got to get on with your new job!"

"What's that?" Dad asked from his meditations.

"Sheriff of St. Francois County!"

"Oh, that," Dad replied and it sounded as if that wasn't the important outcome of this at all.

# All the Beautiful Things

WALKING three miles to Sunday school and back, across the swollen river in the spring, through deep snowdrifts in winter and under the relentlessly hot sun in summer, Lou and I sometimes wondered if we were "getting our money's worth," especially when meadow dews soaked our Sunday stockings, cockleburs matted our shoe laces, and snakes and lizards lay across our path.

We had been taught to put our efforts into the things from which we would get the most durable and lasting benefits. We wore brass-toed shoes to school, for that way we were comfortably shod and one pair would last all winter. A sheet-iron roof was put on the old farmhouse so it would never have to be roofed again. Fancy vegetables in the seed catalogues were looked at, but pole bean, turnip, and tomato seeds were ordered. Emphasis was put on the rugged, hardy, enduring things. All wool and a yard wide. Cast iron, Solid oak.

So it was with some misgivings that we contemplated the benefits of the six-mile journey to Sunday school. School, which was the same distance, we had to attend, but Sunday school was a matter of choice, or rather a matter of Mom's choice. True, we got to put on our prettier dresses, in summer carry our colorful paper Japanese umbrellas and in winter wear gloves instead of the schoolday mittens, but that was not the root of the matter and we knew it.

"We have not exhausted the possibilities," Lou said one Sunday on our way home. Whenever she made such an announcement, squint-eyed, and grim-faced, it was with the finality of Doomsday, the drama of a Shakespearean actress, and the intimation that it was high time we began to do something about it.

"Whatdaya mean, 'exhausted the possibilities'?" I asked.

She always looked at me witheringly whenever I called for an explanation but it was a sort of ritual, and had I not asked she would have been shocked and chagrined as if she had hollered, "First bat" at recess and everyone else had run off to play hopscotch.

"Well—" she said, and that was all until we came to the old rail fence separating our farm from the Stacey's. Here she elected to theorize from the top rail, so I, being already over, had to climb back up.

"We ought to be getting something out of it."

"I know the books of the Bible, the Beatitudes, the Commandments and the Lord's Prayer," I said, eagerly.

"Oh, sure," Lou shrugged. "So does everyone."

"I don't think you ought to shrug about it."

"Well, I don't mean to shrug a—a—shrug. I mean those things are everyone's property. I think there ought to be something personal between you and God and me and God that there isn't between anyone else."

These words were faintly reminiscent of Brother Johnson's latest sermon.

I picked at a loose piece of wood on the rail. When anyone started talking about God I was uneasy for I didn't know who or where God really was. Mama said God was Love. The preacher said He was Power. Miss Tillie, our Sunday-school teacher, said He was the Bread of Life. There was a poem we knew that said, "God's in His heaven—all's right with the world." Yet some said He was everywhere and the preacher prayed for Him to be with us night and day. To a little girl, used to adding up two and two and getting four every time, these indefinite, contradicting things were puzzling.

"Couldn't you and I go together as one?" I asked, not wanting to be separated from Lou for even a minute, and that she should strike up a relationship with God and leave me out would have been unbearable.

"Well, I don't know," she demurred, glancing at me sideways, as if judging my capacity to understand things of the spirit. "See what you can find out about Him."

"Who?"

"God."

"How soon?"

"Any time. Say next Sunday."

But I didn't have any answers by the next Sunday, or the next or the next, and neither did Lou. There was nothing any more personal in our relationship with God than there had been before. We said our prayers, not only the Lord's Prayer but some original prayers of our own, kept the Commandments as best we could, and continued going to Sunday school as usual.

I felt that I was working against time. Any day now Lou was likely to come up with something and leave me out in the cold. In church I kept a wary eye on her, half expecting her to get up and shout like old Grandma Weaver did, or add a hearty "Amen" at the end of the preacher's better statements like some of the older folks did.

But nothing new happened and I thought that Lou had forgotten all about it. Perhaps she had changed her mind and thought we were exhausting the possibilities after all.

With the coming of spring our Sunday-school superintendent decided that for our annual picnic we would make a pilgrimage to McKendree Chapel, an old log-cabin building, the oldest church of our denomination west of the Mississippi River.

This would mean a tremendously long journey of approximately seventy-five miles, a feat never accomplished in lumbering farm wagons or even in the more sprightly buggies. There were not enough automobiles in the community to accommodate the crowd, so two big cattle trucks were commissioned and, in pink and white organdy dresses, with fried chicken, baked beans, and cocoanut cake stacked away in one corner, we set out early in the morning for the historic site.

It was a wonderfully warm, sweet-smelling day. Though the road was rutted and bumpy, around each bend was a fresh new picture of spring—green meadows pinned down with dandelion brooches, grazing sheep on a stumpy hillside, or freshly plowed fields mellowing in the sun.

Later in the morning we passed through communities where people were going to church, some walking, some riding. They waved to us in good fellowship, sensing our mission. We passed by Fredericktown and Lou and I waved in the direction of Grandma Casey's house, but it was only a gesture for she was far off the road. I noticed the freckles popping out on Lou's nose and that her hair was coming loose around her face, softening her features. Maybe this was worth all our trips to Sunday school I thought, this one annual picnic where there would be games and good food and a new countryside.

The old log church sat back from the road in a grove of giant oaks, while lesser trees of dogwood and redbud adorned the outer fringes of the woodland. Buttercups and bluets pushed up through the thick grass and nearby a bubbling spring reflected the delicate tracery of uncurling ferns. It was a fitting place for pioneers to choose to kneel in worship. Off in the surrounding woods we heard the thrush and the blue jays, alarmed at our coming. As we filed reverently through the narrow doorway to inspect the inside, it was not difficult to pretend that we were coming to church a hundred years earlier.

Save for the huge stone fireplace at one end and the long narrow pews, the old building was not a whole lot unlike our smokehouse at home, with its great yellow poplar logs and handmade cypress slab roof. An old tuneless organ stood off to one side and Lou and I stroked it with loving care. We had a similar tuneless instrument at home. We tried out all the seats and wondered how it would be to have a fire in the fireplace at church during services.

"They didn't have stoves then," Jeptha Alexander put in, and was immediately laughed down.

"Well, when was it built?" Jeptha demanded.

Brother Johnson set us straight. "They had camp meetings here first for nearly fifteen years," he said. Then, in 1819, this chapel was built."

"Hummm, back about Jefferson's time," Ray Stacey said.

"Jefferson?" Lou demanded. "Why, he was only our third President."

"That's right," Brother Johnson replied.

We looked at the old building with even greater awe and respect and tread gently upon its wide board floors.

Because of the lateness of our arrival, we had only a brief devotional service outside before the picnic lunch, but afterwards everyone crammed and wedged into the old building until it seemed some would stick out between the cracks like corn in a crib. I was on the back row of the choir and could see only the wall behind me and out the little square-paned window, for Nettie McClanahan, Gus Larkey, and Jeem Hollister loomed big and broad-shouldered in front of me.

We chose hymns we thought may have made the rafters ring a century earlier and Brother Johnson took his text from Isaiah: "In returning and rest shall ye be saved; in quietness and in confidence shall be your strength."

I studied the flowers in Nettie's dress and the way the hair grew in little whirlwinds on the back of Jeem's neck. Tiring of that, I looked at the wall behind me. There were initials carved deeply into the old logs—M. R. and H. W., A. S. and J. T. I thought up names to go with them. There on one log was carved D. Boone. Did it stand for Daniel Boone? Was it possible he had carved it himself? If so, what a relic that log was and would become as time went on. I traced my own initials with my finger, wondering if, had they been real, someone might make up names to fit them a hundred years from now.

Brother Johnson said something and pounded his fist on the altar. A half dozen loud "Amens" followed. I looked anxiously at Lou, sitting down the row from me. She didn't look like she had said anything, so I turned back to the wall.

Now, whose name, I wondered, would have meant more to people if carved here in the log than Daniel Boone's did? Jefferson? He could have, so Ray Stacey had said. He could have sat right here where I was sitting and carved his name. Teacher wouldn't have liked it, though. *Teacher!* This wasn't a schoolhouse. This was a church house. God's house. How would it have been had God carved His name there? That would have made people gather round. I visualized how it would look. Right over Boone's name. Silly me. God couldn't write, could He? Well, silly me again—God could do anything. If He wanted to sign His name somewhere, He who had created the heavens and the earth, He could most certainly do it!

Now, just suppose, I reasoned to myself, that God

wanted to write His name around here to let people know He'd been here. How would He do it? I looked out the window and my gaze fell on a patch of bluets in the grass. Funny, that isolated little patch of bluets like that. Almost like someone had planted them. Well, someone had, of course. God. Maybe that's the way God signed His name. Mr. Kotiski had just made an "X" for his name. Why wouldn't God make a patch of bluets for His? Or a—a—I looked around for other things, excited with the enormity of my discovery. My eyes lifted to a bluebird sitting on a bough.

Sure, there He'd signed His name again. Just for me. I closed my eyes to shut out all other things while I pondered this thought. Several "Amens" sounded and it was as if they were underlining my discovery. A good warm feeling spread over my body. For a horrid moment I thought I was going to cry, right up there in the choir section. I wondered who I ought to tell first about this, if anyone. What fun I was going to have the rest of my life looking for places where God had signed His name. Maybe telling it would spoil it. This was a lovely thing between me and God—why, it was what Lou had meant, a personal thing. I looked down the row at her, observing the dear, familiar, freckled face that could be Pythias, or Ananias, or a Dutch Twin with equal aplomb. Her stubby-fingered hands were folded peacefully in her lap—hands that had tied my shoes, combed my hair and led me confidently across the river; hands that had patched sacks with me, hoed corn, milked cows, carried water. Of course, God had signed His name there in her hands.

All the way back home that day, I saw His signature, written in many forms, like one would write in many languages so that, if one missed it here, it would be there. The meadow lark, balancing on a millet stalk, the hands of the old man loosening a horse's foot caught in the wire fence, the tender way Mrs. McDowell held her baby in the bumping truck, the big pines marching up the hill, the sunset that evening, and the fireflies in the meadow at night.

A few Sundays later, after Lou had already climbed over the old rail fence on our way home from Sunday school, I sat on top and said, "I've got it."

"Got what?" she demanded, climbing back up.

"Something between me and God."

"Whatdaya mean?"

I tried to look at her witheringly, but this I never could do quite as well as she.

"I know where He signs His name."

She looked at me warily, hardly believing, yet not daring to disbelieve.

"See these bluebells. " I pointed to a clump. "He's been there. He signed His name there. And that cloud up there—that's His signature, too." I pointed out many other things, anxious that Lou should share this new knowledge with me. "Everywhere there is something beautiful, He's signed His name," I explained.

"Yeah," she said, slowly at first, but then again, "Yeah," her eyes widening, and again, "Yeah!"

I was glad Lou understood, for now we could hunt together for places where God had signed His name. But whether she had or not, I was no longer skeptical about the worth of the journey to Sunday school, for out of these journeys, with the early questionings and skepticism, had come a most durable, lasting, iron-clad, brass-toed relationship between God and me. For, I reasoned, if we search for Him where He has been, surely we will find Him where He is.

Lou set the table that night for supper and when I sat down I saw it there, gleaming by my plate—the silver spoon.